HAUNTED

A PARANORMAL AWAKENING

JULIE COONS

Haunted: A Paranormal Awakening

Copyright © 2021 by Julie Coons

All rights reserved.

ISBN print: 978-1-7360704-0-6
ISBN e-book: 978-1-7360704-1-3

www.JulieCoons.com

"The day science begins to study non-physical phenomena, it will make more progress in one decade than in all the previous centuries of its existence."

— NIKOLA TESLA

CONTENTS

1

This will be a day I'd come to regret. But then again, how could I have known what I was in for? I believed I reached Nirvana. It was truly a dream come true. I've wanted this for such a long time. I guess all I have to say now is, be careful what you wish for.

It's an unexpectedly warm day for October. Especially unusual for this part of Oregon. We were experiencing a heat wave like no other. Summer came early. The flowers are holding onto their fragrance and some are even still blooming. The changing colors of the leaves on the trees turning from orange to red are the only thing reminding me we are entering fall. What a perfect day today is, driving down this luxurious tree-lined street full of manicured lawns. I'm in awe as I gaze upon some of the biggest, most beautiful hanging baskets I've ever seen. The tall hedges separating these mansions and lining the sidewalks are perfectly manicured. *This is pure elegance.* As we slowly make our way down the street, I can barely take it all in. Not all residential neighborhoods are created equal. This one stood out with its part concrete, part cobblestone sidewalks next to an asphalt that appears to be painted black without a visible speck of dirt on it. Even the cars parked on the road are what one would call upper-class luxury. I'm blinded by the bright sky shining off their curved fenders. I've never seen a Maserati or a Lamborghini in person before. They don't sell cars like these in my old neighborhood. The people strolling down the sidewalk are smiling and waving as we drive by, already making me feel welcome. It looks like something straight out of a Home and Gardens magazine. This neighborhood is named, "Crystal Shores" but I think they should call it "Pleasantville" instead. I wouldn't be surprised if their association has rules against crappy cars like mine parking here, let alone living here. This is one of those places I could only dream of living someday.

The neighborhood is developed around a man-made lake. The lake was previously a rock crushing quarry for many years. When the quarry operation stopped, a local group of developers purchased the property and built the lake. The same builder designed the neighborhood and built the homes. They designed the homes to resemble one another. The finest homes overlook the lake, which is about a mile and a half in circumference and over a thousand-feet-wide. There's even a well-lit walking path that goes around the entire lake. To make the lake look more natural, an island was built in the middle and filled with tall shrubs. Now it's a protected fish and wildlife nature preserve, and many varieties of birds come back every year to lay their eggs. It's a beautiful and natural looking lake. If I hadn't known it was a rock crushing quarry years ago, *because my uncle once worked there*, I never would have been the wiser. They did an incredible job hiding the fact that the lake is man-made, right down to all the shrubbery planted around the shore. The neighborhood provides for 300 homes directly on the lake and more than doubles that amount in the outlining areas. At the opposite ends of the street is a grassy common area with more paths to walk and large, magnificent waterfalls. This neighborhood is a glorious display of homes and nature. It's perfect.

I've driven down this street many times and fantasized, but today is different.

Today, this is my neighborhood.

I've been through a lot as a single parent. I've lived in so many dumps I could barely afford. Forced to live in rat and cockroach-infested nightmares in some of the scariest parts of town. This is the last place a new mother wants for her family. However, I had to get away from my abusive, alcoholic, cheating husband before he killed me. Sometimes there just isn't a choice. I really did my best, but now life is going to get so much better. A lot can change in eight years. Eight very long years.

I left my abusive husband when our daughter was only one. Now I am married to a wonderful man who is also an amazing father to Stephanie. He has built a very successful business from the ground up. Soon we will move to the other side of the tracks, *as they say*. I never allowed myself to even dream this day would ever come. My self-esteem never allowed me to think I belonged in such a lovely place as this. But here I am.

2

My dream home, it's perfect. I can't believe it's almost ours. Construction is finished and the final inspection just completed. We go to escrow tomorrow and we move in this weekend. I stayed behind once everyone left so I could be alone in my gorgeous new home. It doesn't seem real to me. I never dreamed I'd ever get to live in such a magnificent home. It's nice to have the house all to myself. I'm noticing even more cool things about it I'd previously missed. I'm in awe of the details. Here I am the proud owner of a brand-new home built by one of the finest builders in the city. The wood detail alone is something to marvel at.

In just a few short years, I've accomplished so much and come so far. Still, I don't feel like I deserve to live in such an upscale neighborhood. It's not what I'm used to. However, this is still going to be mine in a few short days and I couldn't be more excited. I'm walking on air, floating in a beautiful dream. I feel like a fairy princess who just moved into her castle. When I got to the living room, I stopped to admire the bay front windows when something caught my eye. I quickly snap out of my daydream to notice something strange above the fireplace.

What's that on the mantle?

The sun shined perfectly through the windows to make it look like a beacon of light glowing up from the mantle. I didn't want to admit it, but I had the sense that something was watching me and trying to get my attention. On the top of the fireplace mantle, next to the wall, I saw some raised red markings. The writing looked oddly primitive. The words said either "red dog" or "mad dog" in the most interesting bright crimson color I had ever seen. *It looked like Crayola red on steroids.* I couldn't make out specifically what it said, but the more I studied it, I realized it's most likely just a child's handwriting. I couldn't clean it off right away because we didn't have any cleaning products at the home yet, so I left it. As I walked away from the fireplace, I thought I heard something. I could barely hear it . . . it was so faint. It took me a second to pull myself together and even admit to myself I was hearing strange things in my home. What is happening? That sound I heard; it sounded exactly like a sinister chuckle, as if it were laughing at me or worse, mocking me. It's very unnerving, but I still tried to pass it off as coming from somewhere outside. However, it wasn't coming from outside and deep down I knew it. It was coming from inside the house, all the doors and windows were locked. It's hard to explain, especially to myself, but I knew something wasn't right with my dream home.

What should I do? Should I tell anyone what happened? They will assume I'm crazy. And besides, it's probably just some kid pulling a prank. I need to relax and forget about this entire experience. I will clean the writing off the mantle as soon as I can, and that will be the end of that. This is an exciting time. Time to celebrate, not time to get all stressed out over things I can't explain. I'm probably just overtired and imagining things. I've always had a wild imagination, *or so I've been told.* I've got too much work to do to keep worrying about this, anyway. Time to get back home and finish packing.

The weekend arrived, and we moved in with no more incidents. My dream home was back to being perfect. No more sinister laughter, no nothing. I kept my experience to myself and no one was the wiser. I bought a cleaning product made especially for washing off wax and got to work. It wouldn't wash off. Obviously it's not crayon, but what the heck is it? I tried many different cleansers, but nothing touched it. So, I decided the only other option I had was to paint over it. I put a couple coats of paint on it and in less than a week; the stain started coming back through. How in the world is this penetrating through two coats of paint? I painted it again and again *to my surprise* it came right back through the paint. What could they have used that doesn't get covered up with paint? Who are *"they?"* It took over six coats to stop it from coming back through. This is nuts. What the heck was utilized to write on my mantle? Still, it wasn't enough to convince me to share it with my family. Besides, what could I possibly say? There's an even bigger chance they will think I'm completely off my rocker. I kept it to myself and put it all behind me.

Too bad the peace didn't last for long.

Well, at least I got to enjoy my new home for an entire day. The day after we moved in, I started seeing things out of the corner of my eye. You know that feeling when you expect someone to be there, but when you look nobody's there? My peripheral vision was working overtime. I need to just pass this off as being in new surroundings. I'm probably tired still from the move. However, I realize I am not going crazy or tired, there is something here, I can feel it. I feel cool breezes coming out of nowhere with a sudden drop in temperature. *It's the strangest thing.* When I feel the cold breeze, it blows right across my face every single time.

Two days after we moved in, I started hearing banging and scratching sounds that seemed to be coming from inside the walls. I put my ear up to the wall in the hallway and could almost feel the vibration of movement against my face. Great, our new home already has rodents. Deep down I sensed it wasn't, but since the house had a year warranty, I called the builder. They sent someone out right away to check.

No rodents.

Again, I tried to just pass it off as being in new, *albeit glamorous,* surroundings. I finally finished unpacking and walked around admiring everything. We even bought all new furniture before the move. Everything from top to bottom is brand new. This is a one-story, three-bedroom, two-bath home. It includes a large living room with a family room off the kitchen. It even has a fancy dining room with a glass chandelier above the table. I've never had a dining area before. This house has the largest kitchen I've ever seen with actual wood floors against a cozy carpeted family room. The kitchen is beautifully accented with wainscoting and everything is white. Even the marble counter is all white with small flecks of gray. There's an extra-large master bedroom and adjoining master bathroom that's even equipped with a jetted hot tub and walk-in closet. The living room has an ornately carved fireplace opposite the front bay window with a cozy window seat. From the outside, it looks like an elegant cottage. There's a lovely fountain next to the front door, and the shrubs and lawn are manicured to perfection.

We aren't one of the super-rich houses; those homes are on the lake. We are among the houses across the street, but we are still fortunate enough to have a bit of a view of the lake. Behind our house are five large fir trees that line a perfectly manicured back yard. Big sliding glass doors off the kitchen open onto a huge wooden deck with a state-of-the-art built-in barbecue. The back yard looks like a peaceful oasis. I look forward to spending a lot of time out there.

I've never seen another house like this and I still can't believe I get to live here. It's going to take me a while to get used to it. I still feel so out of place in this beautiful rich paradise. I guess I did something right in my life to deserve the honor of living here. Regardless of how unworthy I feel, I'm still going to do my best to soak it all in and try to enjoy every moment I can.

Who knows what tomorrow will bring . . .

3

Now that everything's unpacked, it's time to hang pictures. I have lots and lots of pictures to hang, so I'd better get started. I'll need help to hang the larger pictures, but I have lots of family photos I want to hang in the hallway. Did I mention the gorgeous hallway yet? I swear this builder didn't miss a beat. He is the quintessential expert at detail. Wainscoting lines the hallway halfway up the wall with art deco crown molding and wide wood trim. All white. The builder must have really loved white because everything here is white. I will eventually put some color on these walls, but for now I will settle with just hanging some pictures.

I had been hanging pictures for about an hour when I noticed some more knocking sounds coming from inside the same wall that I was hanging pictures on. Each time I hammered a nail into the wall, I was getting a knocking response right back. I stopped hammering to see if anything else would happen, but nothing did. I wondered . . . was there just some kind of strange echo coming from inside the wall from my hammer when I hammered a nail against it? So, I tried a brief experiment. I hammered in a nail and then I waited. Each time there came a knocking sound in response. I waited to determine if any more would happen and everything went silent. I hammered another nail and the same thing happened. It felt like I was getting some kind of response in code or something. It even sounds crazy to me, but I just kept on hammering nails to determine what would happen. This continued for about a half hour when I discovered I had close to one hundred nails hammered into the wall. I realized I would have a tough time trying to explain this to my husband when he got home. He would assume I was losing it. So, instead of continuing with my strange experiment, I spent the next hour covering up all the nail holes. I tested it for another few minutes by hanging a few more pictures, but whatever seemed to communicate with me was gone. The knocking had stopped, and it never came back. In a strange way, I felt weirdly disappointed. I wasn't afraid, just extremely intrigued.

As hard as I tried, I just couldn't wrap my head around what had happened. Was anything communicating with me after all? This is all in my head, I was the only one home. What was I thinking? Did I have little elves or leprechauns living inside my walls? That sounds ridiculous even to me, so I decided to never mention it to another person. This stays with me.

The next day I got back to hanging pictures. I was hoping for something to happen, yet fearful it would. I hung a few photos and nothing knocked back. I was feeling a bit oddly disappointed when suddenly there came a knock. It was back, and it was knocking louder than the day before. I was intrigued, but not afraid. I wanted to tear into the wall to see what was knocking at me, but I didn't. How would I possibly explain that? So, I kept on hanging pictures in the hallway and getting knocks back. These knocks were a little different than yesterday. Today, the knocks were coming back in sets of three. I will never forget the last picture I ever hung in the hallway. I finished hammering in the nail, then waited for the knock. What came instead was a loud thud so powerful it knocked a few pictures off the wall. This wasn't anything playful like the knocks from yesterday, this was an angry thud that seemed more sinister. It startled me so much I dropped my hammer on my bare foot and ran as fast as I could to get away from it. I was so terrified I ran out of the house. The message I got from the thud was clear. The message I got? Get the hell out. I stood outside on the front porch next to my gorgeous new waterfall and wondered what waits for me inside my house. What could

I do? Stand outside forever? Eventually I would need to go back inside, even though I'm scared to death. By this time my foot was throbbing.

The scariest part is not knowing what's happening. For me, no matter how bad the situation, if I understand it, I might be able to handle it. This, I have no explanation for. I don't understand it at all. I can't explain it to myself. How could I tell another person without looking crazy?

All I can do is take a moment to breathe and try to calm myself down.

As I sat on the porch in front of my new dream home, a neighbor came over to welcome us into the neighborhood. Such a friendly gesture, but I wasn't in the mood for any small talk with people I just met. The neighbor that came over was our next-door neighbor, and she brought her two adorable daughters with her. "I'm Angela, and these are my daughters, Maddie and Christie."

"What a beautiful family you have, Angela. How old are your daughters?"

"Christie's six and Maddie is two."

Everyone was dressed to the nines just to hang out in their house. She even brought me a pie.

"Thank you so much for making us this pie, that was very thoughtful of you."

I didn't realize people still did stuff like that.

I desperately wanted to ask her if she had any experiences like mine, but how do you ask that question? I just met this woman. I didn't want her to think I was nuts or like she needed to shield her young children from me. It was actually a welcome break to the horror I was feeling. If left to my own devices too long, I can blow a situation way out of proportion with my imagination. So, it was probably a blessing she came over when she did.

"Why are you sitting outside on the porch with no shoes on?"

Because something creepy and evil inside my house scared me to death, so I fled.

I couldn't tell her the truth, so I lied.

"I'm just relaxing and enjoying the waterfall."

That seemed enough for her and after a few more minutes she left. I sensed she wanted to ask me more questions but didn't. She seemed nervous as she talked, but since I'd just met her, how could I know for sure? Something seemed off, and I sensed she wanted to go inside her own home as much as I did mine. We both probably wanted to run away from this place, but neither of us could say so.

This is ridiculous, I'm definitely blowing this out of proportion. I need to get back inside my house and finish hanging pictures. Screw that, I need to go back inside to get my purse and some shoes on so I can escape this place for a while. I called my friend Rosie and asked her to meet me for coffee. I ran in the house, *feeling a chill up my spine* grabbed my purse, opened the garage door and jumped in my car. I put my shoes on while feeling somewhat safer inside my car and drove away. I felt better the moment I got out of the neighborhood. What is really going on here? I hope soon I can understand it, but for now I just need to talk to a friend.

"Hey Jules, how's it going?"

"Great . . . great, everything is great, how are you?"

"Not so sure I believe you, but alright. Everything is great with me, too. How are things with the new house?"

Oh Lord, not this again.

"Fine, I mean, it's great."

"So bottom line, everything is great."

"Well, not exactly. We're all moved in, but I really want to talk about anything other than the house. You know how exhausting moving can be and everything. Tell me about you. How's the new boyfriend?"

"Julie, is everything ok? I'm getting a strange vibe from you that it isn't."

"Rosie, not really. But I don't even know how to explain it to you. When I figure it out, can we talk then?"

"You got it. Just know I'm here for you anytime, day or night."

"I know you are, Rosie. You've been one of my closest friends since when, middle school? I will be ok. I just don't want to talk about it right now."

5

Problem was, what could I say? How would anyone else understand when I couldn't myself?

"Julie, talk to me. I can't relax until I know what's going on with you."

"Ok Rosie, but I want you to know if I tell you I can't un-tell you."

"Spill it."

"I think my house is haunted."

"Oh Julie, that's just because you're in new surroundings and hearing those new house settling sounds. There's no way your brand-new house is haunted. Try to relax and allow yourself to enjoy something for once."

"Yeah, you're probably right."

My friend Rosie and I talked for a long time over coffee. After a couple hours, I had no choice but to head back home. It was a welcome break from all the weirdness I've been dealing with. When I pulled into the neighborhood, that old feeling of nervousness and dread returned. I rounded the corner, got to my house and engaged the electric garage door opener. As the door was opening, I noticed something odd on the garage floor. I left my car outside on the driveway and got out to see what it was. To my amazement, all of our shoes *that were lined up in the garage against the wall when I left* were now arranged in a circle facing inward in the middle of the garage. Perfectly facing one another, it seemed there was some kind of meaning to the way they were arranged in relationship to each other. It looked kind of ritualistic to me in a weird intuition-sort-of way.

Even though this was more intense than the knocks on the wall I still didn't know how to talk to my family about it. I put the shoes back where they belonged and drove my car into the garage, but I still couldn't bring myself to go inside the house yet. I was so afraid of what I might find. I grabbed some yard tools and sat back down on the front porch. At least this time if a neighbor comes over and wonders what I'm doing, I can lie and say I'm doing yardwork. The last thing I wanted to do was go back inside my lovely new home.

I sat there daydreaming about meeting my new next-door neighbor earlier that day. At the same moment, I heard Angela yell at Maddie. I got up and walked to the front of the driveway to see Maddie squatting and peeing in their front yard. I laughed so hard I almost peed my pants, too. In Maddie's defense, she's barely two years old and probably didn't know any better. She was still in diapers, so I yelled over to Angela, "I think Maddie is trying to tell you she's ready for potty training." Her mom just shrugged her shoulders and took Maddie back inside her house. I thought that was a little odd. Could be all in my head, but I thought Angela looked a little stressed.

I went back to sitting on my front porch. I wondered if Angela thought it was strange that I didn't invite her to come inside my house earlier. I made up some lame excuse about it still being a mess and promised to have her over when we were more settled. That never happened. I was getting attached to this family from talking to them outside. We never invited each other into our homes. We only talked to one another outside when her kids were playing on the swing-set in their backyard. Perhaps Angela was feeling the same way I was. One morning I woke up and Angela and her family had left. It looked as if they moved out in the middle of the night. We never saw them again, and to this day we don't know why they left so abruptly like that. Or, should I say, what caused them to leave. I have my opinions, but I'd sure love to know what happened.

The last time I saw Angela was on a Tuesday afternoon and we did the same thing we always did. We stood next to the swing-set, pushing the girls on the swings, and nervously chatted about everything instead of what we wanted to, or should have talked about. A couple days after they left, I saw a big moving truck parked outside their house. I went over to see what was going on. I was told by the owner of the property they'd moved out. They left everything behind, including the dinner dishes that were still sitting on the table. I didn't know they were renting the property next door. I assumed everyone who lived here were homeowners. The house is owned by a man named Dave, and he seemed as perplexed as I was. He invited me to come inside and see for myself.

What I saw floored me, it was so incredibly bizarre. It's like they got up in the middle of eating their dinner and just booked. What would make an entire family do something like that? All I can think is that it must have been something pretty terrifying. Not only did they leave their food on the table, they left their furniture, kitchen utensils, children's toys, all their clothes, everything. They literally got up and ran. I really wish I would have had the guts to ask Angela the question I was dying to ask her. Now it's too late and I will never get the chance again. I'm feeling completely baffled.

What the heck is going on around here?

Nothing much happened in my house of horror after Angela left. It was oddly quiet. No knocks, not even a cool breeze across my face. That's another thing that kept happening to me. I'd be sitting on the couch watching television and a chilly breeze would blow across my face. It could be warm and cozy inside the house, and still I'd feel a strange chilly breeze blowing across my face. Once in a while the breeze would bring an odor with it. Most of the time it was a hideous odor of dirty feet, or a not so great floral smell. It smelled old and pungent, like a rose scented perfume, but one that had spoiled many years ago. I'd ask other people in the room with me if they could smell anything and every single time, they said no. Eventually, I stopped asking.

The smells never alarmed me that much, until the smell that came with the breeze was the nastiest smell I can remember. It smelled of rotting meat. This time it even lingered longer than the other smells did. Usually it was fleeting, and the smell was gone as soon as the breeze stopped blowing on my face. It felt intentional since it always blew across my face. I knew something was trying to get my attention, *but what?*

The thing that bothered me the most is how these experiences only seemed to happen to me and usually when I was all alone in the house. I asked Jeff a few times if he felt comfortable here. Most of the time he just looked at me like I needed some counseling. I asked Stephanie if she enjoyed living here, and she said she loved our new home. Stephanie was only in middle school so I didn't think it was appropriate to discuss anything with her, let alone ask her too many questions about strange activity. The last thing I wanted to do was scare her. She was adjusting very well to her new school, and I was grateful. One of the primary reasons we moved to this neighborhood was because of the school system. She was bullied terribly at the last school she attended, and I had no choice but to take her out of there.

I really tried to get some help before removing her. I reached out to the school counselor first and when I got nowhere with her, I went to the school principal. I even went to her teacher for help and nobody did a thing about it. I eventually paid a visit to the mother of the bully, but she believed her daughter. Nobody would help me, and Stephanie was growing more depressed with each passing day. She was faking illnesses to stay home, and later I found out her bully was getting other little girls to join in. Kids can be very cruel and with no help from any of the adults at the school, we pulled her out. It ended up being the smartest thing we've ever done, but what did I just move her into? I pray whatever is here leaves my daughter alone. She's been through too much already at such a young age.

4

W e had been in the house for about a month now and we were finally getting settled. I haven't had any weird things happen lately, so I was thrilled with the peace. Jeff was at work, Stephanie was at school, so I decided it was the perfect time to clean the house. It desperately needed cleaning. How three people can dirty up a house so fast is beyond me.

At least Stephanie has already made friends with an amiable group of girls at her new school and they feel welcome coming to our home. That made it so special for me, too. I love being a mom. I love having her friends over for dinner, sleepovers, anything they want, the more the merrier. I just hope nothing major happens here to scare them away. It would be tragic if Stephanie lost these friends. Time will tell, but for now I just need to keep calm and pray it doesn't.

I'm finishing up my dusting when I get to the last room; the living room with the gorgeous bay front window. This is my favorite room. It's the most relaxing place to be in the house, especially early in the morning when I drink my coffee. I sit on the window seat and watch the neighbors leave for the day. I feel like I'm the only one left on my street after watching so many cars go by, which only adds to my nervousness. But why? It's not like I would run to any of my neighbors for help. I wouldn't want any of them to know anything, they'd think their new neighbor was a lunatic. Unless they are experiencing some of the same things. I suspect that's why Angela and her family moved out. Something had to terrify them so badly they just ran and left everything behind.

There have been moments when I've seriously wondered about my own mental health. It's easier to think I'm imagining the things I've experienced than try explaining it. Besides that, what could I possibly say? I think my brand-new house is haunted? It didn't turn out so well when I told Rosie. Why would anyone else be any different?

I dusted the gorgeous new glass tables next to our cozy cream-colored leather couch and love seat. I dust the matching silver metal lamps standing on the beveled glass insert inside the tables' silver metal frames. I admire how closely the metals match. So much luxury. I positioned the love seat opposite the Bayfront window, so it's very cozy and inviting in here. At the other end of the living room is a large dining room. We have a long wood table with matching chairs big enough to hold family or friends for special dinners. I'm so happy I have enough room now to host a dinner party. I placed a large wicker basket on the table for now. Just until I find the perfect thing for it.

The fireplace in the room is the other main focal point beside the bay window. There's a large oval mirror above the mantle and it looks stunning. I decorated the mantle with photos, a lovely blue glass vase, a couple Victorian antique figurines and a long narrow crystal bowl. Not just your run-of-the-mill everyday knick-knacks, that's for sure. Jeff is really the one with the eye for design. If it weren't for Jeff, I'd still have the bric-à-brac I picked up from the local second-hand store that I've carried around with me for years. It's hard to get used to this alternative way of life. Not that I'm complaining, because I'm not . . . I'm grateful. I just think some things aren't necessary and expensive items are an exorbitant waste of money. I feel guilty if I spend money on frivolous items. After all, there are starving people in the world.

I was dusting the mantle when something stuck out to me as odd. I could remember where I placed each item, but the items now appeared to have moved around. Not moved that much, just enough to notice. But then again, I could be wrong. I put the thought out of my mind. I moved the items back to their original places on the mantle and went about my work. It's also possible that someone else in the house could have moved it. When I came back into the living room to finish the last of my chores, I could have sworn the objects had moved again. This time I came up with a genius idea. I would draw a line around each item with a pencil so if it moves again, I will know for sure.

The next morning, I walked into the living room to sit on the window seat to drink my morning coffee. As I took my first sip of coffee, I thought I saw something move out of the corner of my eye. It was a black shadow moving across my peripheral vision, leading my eye toward the mantle. I got up and to my amazement, nearly every item on the mantle had, in fact, moved. I was stunned it actually worked. Ok, so this really is happening. *Now what?* Do I talk to my family about it? I don't even know how to begin that conversation. For now, I will keep this to myself. I don't want to say anything to Stephanie just yet. If I talk to anyone it will be Jeff, but why bother. He's so damn skeptical. *It's so annoying.* In my opinion, most men are skeptics. I doubt he'd believe me anyway, so why the hell should I bother?

Saying I don't have a good relationship with my mother would be an understatement. Professionals diagnosed us as having a love-hate relationship. I'm closer to my father even though he did nothing to get my mother mental help or protect us kids from her. I think he was even more afraid of her than we were. I also have a brother who's three years older than me. We don't really know each other anymore and he lives far away in Las Vegas. I don't blame him. He wanted to get as far away from this life as possible, and he succeeded. I wasn't so lucky.

Later that afternoon, I invited my parents over for dinner to see our new home. My father was a retired real estate agent, and I knew he'd appreciate all the beauty and over-the-top detail this house possessed. I was excited for him to see the new mansion we were living in. All my life I yearned to make my father proud of me, and this time I think I succeeded. They didn't live too far from us, but this was their first opportunity to see it.

I gave them a tour and my father gave me more compliments than I expected from him. He was really impressed, and that made me feel so happy. My mother wouldn't give me a compliment if her life depended on it. Whatever, I'm used to it. I wanted to see my father, and she was the unfortunate baggage that came along with him.

My father wasn't an enormous man, neither was my mother. Dad was perpetually thin no matter what he ate, and boy could he eat. He was always the first and the last one at the dinner table. We wasted no food when he was around. Dad always dressed to the nines, as did my mother. Fashion was very important to them. Outward appearances meant everything to my parents. I'm sure as a teen I took every opportunity to embarrass and challenge them. I wasn't a bad kid, just a bit rebellious. Mostly, I aimed my intense bitterness at my mother. In my defense, who could blame me? My mother was a horrible excuse for a mother and repetitively told me my father never wanted me and she wished I had died at birth. Some people should never have children.

I'm a daddy's girl. I'm sure my mother was jealous of my relationship with my father. It even sounds sick and twisted to me, but what could I do about it? I was just a kid. My father was raised in a strict Catholic home. As were we. My brother and I both had to attend Catholic grade school until the sixth grade. Getting out of private school was like getting out of prison. I think it did some amount of damage to us both.

We were about to sit down to eat the lasagna dinner I had prepared, my father's favorite, when we all heard a loud crashing sound coming from the living room. At the same time, my father came running into the kitchen. I swear, when I first saw his face, he looked as white as our walls and his eyes were open wider than I'd ever seen.

"Dad, what's wrong?"

He was out of breath as he tried to get his words out. I got him a glass of cold water and led him over to sit down on the couch.

"Take your time, Dad, it's ok. You can tell us when you're ready."

After a few sips of water and some deep breaths, he was ready to talk.

"I don't know what just happened, but I think I just saw your wicker basket go flying off your dining room table."

I just sat there for a moment, dazed. I didn't know what to say, and I am rarely at a loss for words. I believed my father. He's never lied to me. Poor guy, I looked over at him and he was visibly shaken and incredibly upset. I almost felt frozen in the new reality of what just happened. I was also afraid of how my husband and daughter would react to the new knowledge that something is terribly wrong with our new home.

As usual, my husband just deflected to Dad accidentally bumping it off the table and he made it fall. My daughter didn't say anything, and that worried me. I got the feeling she wasn't that surprised. Perhaps Jeff wasn't the first person I needed to talk to about this.

Dad looked at me like he was waiting for a response, but I still didn't know what to say. I knew something had happened, yet I still played it off as if maybe he accidentally bumped it and knocked it off the table.

After what seemed like a longer than normal period of silence, we all walked into the living room and sure enough, there was the wicker basket laying on the floor.

"Dad, are you sure you didn't just accidentally knock it off the table?"

"Julie, I may be old, but I'm not senile. I know what I saw and I know, sure as shit, I saw your wicker basket fly off your table."

"I know, Dad, I believe you."

I patted my father on the back, and that was enough to reassure him. After all I've already experienced in this house, how could I not believe him? This was just the beginning of all the unexplainable things that happened in our house. Definitely the tamest compared to what was coming.

My poor father. He was so shook-up he could barely eat his dinner.

Not another word was spoken about the wicker basket.

Mom didn't have much to say about it, which didn't surprise me at all. Her favorite subject was herself. It upset me this happened to Dad. Why couldn't it have happened to her instead? Whatever or whoever's here is probably terrified of my mother.

I couldn't say anything though, especially since I had mentioned none of my experiences to anyone yet. I just let everyone think Dad was mistaken. No way does a wicker basket go flying off a dining room table all by itself. *Or does it?*

Mom and Dad left shortly after dinner.

My father was so sure he saw something he called his parish priest first thing in the morning. He set up an appointment for the priest to come bless our house that same day. Not just any priest either, he called the priest my father considered the big kahuna, the head priest for our town, Father Rainey. What could I say, no?

My father went to a lot of trouble to do this for us, and besides, maybe it will do some good. I was a practicing Catholic growing up, but since I hated the torture I endured in Catholic school, I now refer to myself as a "recovering Catholic." However, I still believe in God and the sacraments of the church.

"Alright Dad, if you feel that strongly I will be here this afternoon for Father Rainey."

Now, I need to explain it to my husband. He's not religious at all, but I don't think he will mind too much. *I hope.*

"Your father did what?"

"Jeff, it's really no big deal. Most Catholics have their homes blessed even before they move into them. You know Dad was really upset over what he saw and this is just his way of making sure we are all protected. I really don't see what it will hurt."

"OK, Julie, but I don't want your Dad thinking it's alright to keep butting into our business."

"Well, I really don't think Dad was 'butting' into our business this time, Jeff."

I was trying not to get too defensive of my father because that could open up another can of worms. I don't need to deal with more crap on top of everything else that's going on right now. It seems as though ever since we moved into our new dream home things have been a lot more tense between us. I didn't understand why, but I fear it might have something to do with the house. I know Jeff is a little sensitive about my father ever since he felt judged and spied on by my parents. One afternoon, Mom and Dad saw Jeff on the golf course when they thought he should have been at work instead. Jeff owns his own company. Jeff runs a very successful janitorial business. He has the freedom to come and go when he wants to, as long as things are running smoothly. My father also doesn't understand that most of his work takes place in the evening hours when everyone has left their offices for the day. My father is old-school and doesn't understand that. It doesn't give my father the right to judge, but I know he was just looking after his daughter and granddaughter. I understood where Dad was coming from, but Jeff, not so much.

That afternoon I met Father Rainey at the front door. I almost didn't recognize him. It had been so long since I saw the man. I was a little hesitant to allow him inside the house. I'm concerned for his safety, but I was even more fearful his presence might anger something here. I don't really know why I felt this; it was just my ever-present intuition at work. I felt oddly uncomfortable having a priest inside my home. I did everything in my power to brush that off and helped him inside.

"Father Rainey, it's sure been a long time."

The best thing about Father Rainey was his Scottish accent.

"Julie my dear, you're still alive I see. Wouldn't know, hadn't seen you in church for a very long time. You know, your grandma attended church every single day of her life."

"Yes, I know, Father, I know."

My grandma didn't drive, so she walked at least three miles every single day to attend the early morning mass at Saint Joseph's Catholic Church in the heart of our city. She also dressed up in dresses or suits for church and walked the entire way in her black patent leather high-heeled shoes. She was the most faithful woman I've ever known. After mass, she walked the three miles back home. Every day, it didn't matter if it was raining or snowing. She faithfully went to church *every single day*. Nothing stopped her from going until the day she died. I had just turned six years old.

"Shall we get to work blessing your house?"

Yes, please let's get this over with.

"Thank you for blessing my home today, Father, I will be sure to put a donation in Sunday's collection plate."

"Oh, so we will see you in church again?"

I really shouldn't lie to a priest.

"Yes, of course."

Father Rainey began blessing our home. He sat his big black leather bag down and pulled out his aspergillum and aspersorium. The aspergillum is an instrument priests use to sprinkle holy water with. They hold the instrument in their hand and shake it in the direction they want the holy water to go. The aspersorium is the bucket that holds the holy water. It amazed me how old and ornate these instruments looked.

"Father, how old are these items?"

"They were given to the church special from the Vatican. They're at least three hundred years old and specially blessed by the Pope himself."

Well, at least I'm getting the works.

He walked through each room in constant prayer, spreading holy water throughout. It was fascinating to watch. He used blessed oil to draw a cross above each door. As he moved from room to room, he either spoke or chanted in Latin. By the end of the walk, even I felt reborn. It was incredibly revitalizing and gave me a sense of real protection. Not one weird thing happened while the priest was here. Not even a bang, nothing. It was like whatever is here knew the priest was too and didn't want to be noticed, or acknowledged, in any way. I could feel it though, and I sensed it was pissed.

5

Two weeks have gone by since the blessing from Father Rainey. I believe whatever was here bothering me isn't any longer, and I couldn't be more grateful. I even started going back to church again. I thought going to church was helping to keep the peace in my home. It really wasn't, but I wanted to believe it was.

I had just returned from getting groceries at the local grocery store. I was feeling a bit shook-up because of someone I saw there. Luckily, she didn't see me. It was our old next-door neighbor Donna, another one of the reasons we moved. She was a nightmare. Our girls used to play together, however, it didn't last long. Her daughter, Amber was only ten, and I agree that it's hard to imagine a little girl being abusive, but this one had a dark side.

One day they were playing in the backyard on their trampoline. I was ironing my husband's work shirts in the back bedroom. I heard Stephanie scream, "Mom help" at the top of her lungs, so I ran outside to see what was going on. Stephanie's leg was stuck through one of the holes on the edge of the trampoline and Amber was spraying her in the face with the hose nozzle on full blast. I looked over at Amber and she was laughing and enjoying it. I ran over to the faucet and quickly turned off the water. I pulled Stephanie out of her trap and we went home.

This was the last straw. These girls needed a time-out. Usually they played well together, but this is unacceptable. After I calmed Stephanie down, I went back over to their house to speak to Amber's mother. Donna wasn't home. I didn't realize the mother hadn't been home the entire afternoon. I never would have allowed Stephanie to play alone inside a house with no supervision.

I was steaming mad when Donna finally pulled in her driveway at 6:30 p.m. As I approached their front door, I tried to take in some calming breaths before I talked to her, I didn't want to come across as too enraged. *Even though I was.* I rang the doorbell, and she answered.

"What do you want? I have a headache and I don't want to talk right now."

I tried to explain what happened with the girls and she didn't want to hear it.

"I just think we should give the girls a little time away from each other."

That's when the drama began. Donna came outside when Jeff was working in the yard and flirt with him every chance she got. One day she went on a rampage yelling at other neighborhood kids while they were playing in front of our house because she knew it would rile me up. She parked her car in front of our driveway to trap me in, but the worst thing she did was call the police on me. I lost count how many times she made some crazy story up about me and called the police. The most embarrassing part about this was, her new husband was best friends with my ex-boyfriend who happened to be a cop.

One night in the middle of preparing our dinner, came a knock at the front door. I heard a deep voice say, "I'm looking for Julie, is she here."

I walked to the door and saw an officer standing there. *What the hell now,* is all I could think. He asked me if we could talk somewhere private. I directed him into our garage and sat down on the step leading into the house.

"What's this about, officer, what did my idiot neighbor say about me this time."

All the officer said in return was,

"You have the right to remain silent, anything you say can and will . . ."

What the hell? Is he reading me my Miranda rights right now? I was sobbing uncontrollably and could barely speak.

"Officer, please tell me what this is about."

"Julie, did you leave a note on your neighbor's front door?"

"Yes."

"You're being arrested for trespassing."

"Trespassing, how do you figure?"

"You've been ordered to stay off her property."

"No, I haven't."

Is this happening to me right now? This doesn't seem real.

"I've never been told I can't step foot on her property, not even once . . . and by the way, officer, did you read the note I left her? I was asking her for a truce, for her to stop terrorizing me and my family."

"It doesn't matter what the note said, you still were trespassing. You've been arrested for 'trespass two' and I have decided under the circumstances to release you to your own recognizance."

Ok, so should I thank you for not hauling me off in handcuffs in front of all my neighbors?

"Julie, between me and you, can I give you a piece of advice?"

Between my sniffles I shook my head yes . . .

"Just move. Find another place to live and move. She's out to get you and until you're out of sight and out of mind, she's never going to leave you alone."

"Thanks officer, I agree."

And with that, he shook my hand, wished me well and left.

I think even the officer thought it was ridiculous to arrest me, but what could he do? They ordered him to arrest me, and that's what he did. Later, I was told it was actually my ex-boyfriend who ordered my arrest. That was shocking since he's the one who cheated, and broke up with me years before. What the hell did I ever do to him? *Oh, wait a minute.* Knowing him, he was just showing off and trying to act like a big man in front of his friend. I never did a thing to him to deserve what he did to me, not a thing. All I have in my mind now is . . . revenge.

We had to pay over three thousand dollars for legal representation. I barely made it to the courthouse on time the day of my trial. I was having the worst diarrhea in my life; all night and into the morning. I'm sure it was just nerves. I was terrified. We met our lawyer outside the courthouse. We chatted with her for a few minutes and I think she could see I was scared. She offered to go in and get us registered while Jeff and I waited outside. A few minutes later, the lawyer returned with the biggest smile on her face.

"Julie, the judge threw out your case."

I burst into tears and almost collapsed onto the ground.

Jeff and I went home and put our house up for sale that very afternoon.

The house sold in sixteen days. We sold it ourselves with some free advice from my father. He was even surprised how fast it sold. I wasn't surprised at all, I was motivated to get the hell out. I had planned open houses for every single weekend until it sold. I couldn't get away fast enough.

Between the time the house sold, and we were free, our lovely neighbor made another call to the police. Later that night, there was another knock at my door.

Here we go, again.

"Hello officers, what can I do for you?"

My husband answered the door and tried his best to sound friendly.

"We are here to speak to your wife, again."

"Julie, come to the door."

Jeff sounded stressed.

"Hello officers, what did she accuse me of doing today?"

"Julie, we are quite upset with you. We came by to talk to you this afternoon and you refused to answer your door."

Refused?

"Officer, first of all, I wouldn't refuse to answer the door when police officers are on my porch in the middle of the day. I'm the only one here and how do I know you're not here to tell me someone I love has been in a car accident or something worse?"

"Sure Julie, but we also saw you move the blinds when we rang the doorbell."

Oh Jesus, that was just our dog.

"Did you also hear a dog barking? If our blinds are closed, our dog Pete will move them to see who's at the front door. I'm sure you have mistaken me for our dog."

I think they realized how ridiculous they were sounding by accusing me of doing something I clearly didn't and finally moved on to why they were there.

"We came by to speak with you today because your neighbor accused you of threatening to cause her bodily harm."

Holy shit, how do I keep from laughing?

"Officer, how in the world could I possibly hurt her? First, there's a vast difference in our builds, her being a big fat piece of shit who could sit on me and kill me, and then there's me. I'm barely a hundred pounds soaking wet. How in the world . . . can we get real for a second? What's it going to take for you guys to realize she's just making up lies about me?"

"Yeah, I guess you've got a point."

"We see the sold sign out on your lawn, are you moving soon?"

"As soon as we can, yes officers. Isn't it obvious we are moving just to get away from her?"

～

Just today, I saw that bitch Donna shopping for groceries at MY grocery store. I moved ten miles to get away from that disaster. What in the hell is she doing here? I need to get some answers.

I called my old neighbor Christine. She lived next door to us on the other side. Christine was a gracious lady, and I considered her a friend. She's also a counselor and way too smart to get in the middle of me and Donna.

"Hey Christine, how's it going?"

"Omg Julie, I was just thinking about you. I wanted to call and tell you the latest, but I'm a little fearful of how you will take the news."

"Has it got something to do with Donna? I just saw her when I was shopping at the grocery store near my home today."

"Oh shit, Jules, you alright?"

"I'm pretty shook-up, Christine. Do you know any reason she would have to shop so close to where I'm living now? Who makes a ten-mile drive for groceries, especially when there's a grocery store less than half a mile from her house?"

"Julie, sit down, I've got something to tell you. Donna doesn't live here, anymore. She is now living in your town and not very far away from where you live."

"Shut the hell up! Christine, please tell me you're joking."

"I'm not joking, I really wish I didn't have to tell you this."

"What is happening? First, why did she move, and second, with all the towns in the world, why did she have to choose mine?"

Maybe Donna is why all the strange things are happening in my new home. I bet she put some weird curse on me. *That bitch, I bet that's it*. But how in the world could she? We used to be friends, and as far as I know, she wasn't into any kind of witchcraft. However, if she could lie and get me arrested, she's capable of just about anything; including witchcraft, or voodoo, or who knows what else. What if she cast some kind of spell on me and just wanted to live close enough to observe the terror she's putting me through? What if she got her hands on something diabolical?

What if . . .

I'm sure I'll never know.

"Christine, do you know where Donna and her family are living now?"

"No, sorry. I'll ask around and if I find out anything, I will let you know."

What a strange feeling I had when I hung up the phone. I need to talk to Jeff. This is too weird.

6

"Jeff, guess who I just saw at the grocery store?"

"Julie, I'm really busy right now."

"I just saw Sasquatch, I mean Donna. She was shopping at the grocery store down the street. I called Christine when I got home and she told me Donna and her family just moved to the same town as us."

"Oh, hell no."

"Yep, she's following us. I know that sounds crazy, but I feel like she's stalking me. I want nothing to do with her so now I have to find a different grocery store to shop at."

"I would."

"I'll let you get back to work, we can talk more when you get home."

"K, love you, bye."

"Bye."

I was so exhausted I fell asleep on the couch. It didn't feel like I was asleep very long when I was jolted awake by the sound of someone entering the house.

I heard the door to the garage open. A few seconds later, it slammed shut. I could hear heavy footsteps coming up the hallway toward me. Then I heard Jeff's voice, clear as a bell, calling out my name.

"Julie?"

"Yes babe, I'm in the family room."

A few more footsteps, then nothing. And, strangely enough, nobody appeared, either.

"Jeff, hello, where are you?"

I sat still for a moment, completely stunned. I called out to Jeff again, but still no answer. After a few moments of rising anxiety while I sat frozen to the couch, I stood up. I thought I should go investigate, but I was too afraid to. I rubbed my eyes, then pinched my cheek to make sure I was awake. *Yep, I'm awake.* I called out to Jeff again. Still no response. With shaking legs, I began walking toward the entrance to the hallway. I was thinking someone had broken in and I needed to protect myself so I picked up the baseball bat Stephanie left leaning against the wall.

I peeked around the corner. Absolutely nothing, nobody was there. I slowly ventured a little further down the hallway. The only bedroom someone could have slipped into was Stephanie's which is on the right side of the hallway. I came to her bedroom door and pushed it open a little. One last time I called out for Jeff, but still no answer. I called out again . . .

"Hello? Is anyone there?"

Silence. I walked past Stephanie's bedroom and cautiously made my way into the utility room. I thought I heard a noise behind me, but when I turned to look, no one was there. I slowly opened the door to the garage to see if Jeff's car was there. It wasn't in the garage. I ran back down the hallway toward the front of the house to look out the bay window to see if he had parked his car on the driveway instead. Again, no Jeff. His car was nowhere to be found.

At that moment, I realized Jeff was never here. *So, who was it?* How in the world did I hear Jeff's voice if he wasn't even here? If it was someone else, they did a perfect job mimicking him. This was extremely bewildering. I began noticing that I was really struggling to concentrate. My head felt foggy and I couldn't think straight. Even though I was feeling oddly dazed, I still knew I needed to get the hell out of here. Someone was most likely still inside our home, but my legs just wouldn't move. I'm feeling completely frozen in fear. I've never felt fear like this before, and that's saying a lot. I've been through some real scary shit in my life. I'm standing inside the bay window in my living room, completely frozen and unable to get my legs to move when I sense something ice cold moving up my back. It felt like an icy finger slowly moving from the middle of my spine, up the back of my neck, stopping at the base of my skull. Then I felt it caressing my neck. I was shivering from head to toe. *What the hell?* It freaked me out so badly, but at least it snapped me out of my mental haze and back to reality. I don't know what just happened to me, but I'm not sticking around to find out. I desperately need to get the hell out of here.

I fear my life is in danger.

I grabbed my purse off the kitchen counter and ran like hell out the front door. I was in such a hurry, I tripped and nearly fell off the porch. At the same time, I thought I heard faint laughter coming from the direction of the house. It was a sound I would equate to that of an old witch's cackle, but very muffled. It seemed so far away and unclear that I just wanted to believe I imagined it. I already had enough to deal with. I was shaking so hard by the time I made it to the car, I could barely get my car key in the door. I don't know if I even remembered to lock the front door, but I wasn't going back to find out. I finally got inside the car, started the engine and backed out of the driveway. As I drove away, I looked over at the house fully expecting to see a face in the front window. I didn't see anyone. Something is terribly wrong. I don't think we have an intruder anymore. *This is paranormal.* I also felt as though something was trying to control my mind. I was standing there completely frozen and unable to do a thing about it. I also thought I saw a dark shadow move quickly behind me out of the corner of my eye. I don't understand this at all. It makes no logical sense. Maybe I'm losing my mind because it sure feels that way.

How do I possibly explain this to another person? Especially my skeptical husband. He'll never believe me. I really wish I could talk to our old neighbors, the ones who moved out in the middle of the night. I bet they would understand. I never needed anyone more than I do them right now. I don't even know where to turn for help. Who could help me? I'm feeling desperate to find my neighbors, but where on earth could they be? I fear whatever was terrorizing them is now focused on me.

I think I need to pull over and call the police. Just to make sure nobody is inside our house. I mean, nobody living. I pulled into the grocery store parking lot. Luckily, my cell phone was still inside my purse. I dialed 911.

"911 what's your emergency?"

"Hi, I think there might be an intruder inside my home."

"Are you inside your house now?"

"No, I got out. I ran out the front door so fast I didn't even bother to lock it."

"Please give me your address and I'll get an officer over there right away."

I gave them my address and thanked them. They told me to stay put until I hear all clear from the officer. I'm more than happy to stay away from that dream home of mine.

Stephanie will get out of school soon so I will have to go back home, but for now I'm happy to sit in the parking lot. Lord, what am I going to do? I'm terrified to go home. I'm afraid to tell my family about this, and I don't have a clue how to handle any of it. At least I knew what to expect with my crazy fat bitch of a neighbor. *But this?* I'm not feeling at all equipped to handle it. Where do I go from here and who in this big wide world could save me?

An hour went by before I heard again from the police department. The officer who checked out our home called to tell me they found nobody inside, and it was safe to return. He asked me more questions that I couldn't answer. He must have thought I was just a bit of a head case. Hell yeah, I'm a head case. At least I felt like one.

Mr. Officer, with all due respect, you go through what I just did and come out the other end somewhere close to normal. If you can handle it, more power to you, you're a lot tougher than me.

7

"Jeff, I want to move."

"Julie, we can't afford to move, you know that."

"I know, but I don't feel safe here and I believe a person's home needs to be their sanctuary, their safe place to fall, so to speak. I'm terrified here all the time. I can't sleep, I keep hearing things and this stuff is really freaking me out."

"Julie, you know the police did a full check and nobody was here."

"Jeff, there's something I need to tell you."

I told him about the mimicking of his voice, the footsteps up the hall, the cold icy finger up my back and feeling like something was trying to control my mind.

"Jeff, you've got to believe me. I'm not lying. You have to know I wouldn't ever make any of this stuff up. What reason would I have to do that? I loved this home when we first moved in. I never imagined I'd ever get to live in such a beautiful place. But now, my beautiful dream home has become my nightmare and I really don't know how much more I can take. Please, please Jeff, I need you to believe me."

I just know he's going to think I'm crazy.

"Julie, calm down, I believe you."

"Don't patronize me you son of a bitch, just don't. This is too important. We could be in real trouble here. You know our neighbors moved out in the middle of the night and nobody knows where they are. Hell, they left their dinner plates right where they sat and got up and fled. They didn't even bother to pack the diapers. That tells me they were scared out of their wits and had to get out, fast."

"Julie, we don't know what really happened with the neighbors."

"But I know. I know how they felt because I felt the same way when I fled from this house yesterday out of pure genuine fear. Fear like I've never felt before. I was so afraid at one point I couldn't even walk. I felt like whatever was here was controlling me and keeping me a prisoner in my home. Jeff, I literally could not walk. I now understand the true meaning of being frozen in fear."

"Julie, I think it's time I share something with you. I didn't want to say anything, but I had an experience in the bathroom the other night that I can't explain. I don't want to scare you, but I need to tell you this, so you know I'm on your side and I that I absolutely believe you."

What the hell?

"Jeff you had an experience, too?"

"Yes."

I can't believe what I'm hearing. I'm a little ashamed to say so, but I'm feeling relieved something happened to him, too. This is putting my mind at ease for the first time since we moved here.

"When? Why didn't you tell me about it already?"

"It happened around a week after we moved in, right about the same time you covered up the red markings on the fireplace mantle."

"Oh, ok. I'm dying to know what happened."

"Well, I was in the bathroom brushing my teeth right before bed. I was standing at the sink when I felt a tug on the end of my t-shirt. I looked around thinking you were doing it, but nobody was there. Then, a few minutes later, I could have sworn I heard a chuckle that sounded like it was coming from far off in the distance."

"Wow, Jeff, that's incredible. Why didn't you tell me about this?"

"I don't know, I guess I didn't want to scare you. Plus, I was struggling to believe it myself."

Yeah, I know the feeling . . .

"Jeff, do you think something paranormal is here?"

"I don't know. I don't want to go so far to say or even think that. We invested a lot of money in this house. I'd hate to think it's haunted or cursed or something."

"I agree Jeff, but I know something is going on here. *Something bad.* I'm going to get to the bottom of it. My family is too important to stick my head in the sand and ignore it. I need help and I hope you're on board. I need a teammate and some moral support. I desperately need to stop feeling so alone. I'm so relieved it's not just me that's experiencing things here. Do you think we should talk to Stephanie, or are you worried it might scare her?"

"Let's give it some time. I don't think she's had any experiences, so why say anything that might scare her. Let's keep this to ourselves for now."

I really don't want to live here anymore, but we obviously can't afford to pack up and leave. Also, how could I, in good faith, sell my home to another unsuspecting family? I could disclose the activity, but who'd want to buy it? I suspect it has something to do with the land the house is built on. It can't possibly be the home since its brand new. Besides, I really want to find out what's going on here and the only way I can do that is to stay.

"Ok Jeff, I agree."

For now.

8

I woke up the following day to the sound of multiple sirens screeching down our street. One after another, police cars, a fire truck and an ambulance; all heading down to the same spot at the end of our street. All blaring out the sound of panic as they drove to their intended destination. I even saw a news truck from our local affiliate. Something big must be going on. I never expected to see a sight like this in my upscale new neighborhood. I never even saw anything this dramatic in my old one. I looked out the front window to see most of my neighbors gathering outside on the sidewalk. Everyone was looking down toward where all the action was and they all had one thing in common, they all looked scared.

I put my slippers on and went outside to see what was going on. I didn't want to get chummy with any of my new neighbors yet, not after what happened to me in my old neighborhood, but there was this one special neighbor I just couldn't help but like. Her name is Maggie, and she lives across the street. She's the kindest woman I've ever met. Very strong in her faith, yet not judgmental at all. She was the type of person you just instantly had to like. I ran over to her side of the street and had to search for her among the ever-growing crowd milling around on the sidewalk. All of us nosy looky-loos trying to get a glimpse at what was going on. I was feeling a little ashamed for being a part of it. People were driving down the street craning their necks to see. Why are people so nosy? I guess it's just human nature to want to look, however, I'm most afraid of what I'm about to learn. I have a sinking feeling in my gut something terrible is happening. I'm not psychic at all. Maybe it's "mom's intuition" or just one of those feelings that can't be explained.

As soon as I made my way to the other side of the road, I heard a loud roaring sound coming down the street. Everyone got silent, and we all turned to look. A large boat was being towed, slowly making its way down the street to join all the other emergency and rescue vehicles. When the boat passed by us, we could see the words "water rescue" written on the side of it. Just reading those words gave me chills down my back. I looked at the faces of some of my neighbors and I could see they were feeling as chilled and I was. I knew a rescue boat meant someone has drowned in our lake, or they are still attempting to save someone. Whichever it was, it wasn't good.

"Maggie, that's a water rescue boat, what the heck's going on?"

"I'm not sure yet, but some neighbors said they heard a young boy has drowned in the lake."

"Our lake?"

"How in the world? It's not that big, there's absolutely no undercurrent."

And, stuff like that isn't supposed to happen here.

I got another shiver up my spine remembering Stephanie and her friends had been playing down at the lake yesterday afternoon. This is such a small lake. Boats aren't even allowed in it, only row boats and rafts. No motors were allowed. Well, not until today. People are always swimming and playing in the water. I never had a problem allowing my daughter to play there before. I shouldn't jump to conclusions, I will wait until we know for sure. I went home and waited until we heard something definitive. I really don't want to get to know these neighbors anyway, I'm still too gun shy. About four hours later, this happens:

Breaking news from the local channel two news station . . .

"We interrupt your viewing to bring you some breaking news. A local boy's body has just been recovered from the man-made lake in the Crystal Shores neighborhood. They called divers in earlier today and after dragging the lake for most of the afternoon, they recovered his body. Authorities report he had just recently moved into the neighborhood with his family. Family and friends are shocked he drowned since they considered him to be their best swimmer on his high school's swim team. They scheduled an autopsy for tomorrow. Our thoughts and prayers are with his grieving family."

Such a tragedy.

Stephanie will not be playing in or around that lake ever again. No matter how much she begs. How could I know what lurked in the lake? Something horrible, I imagine. If it could kill an excellent swimmer like the boy down the street, what could it do to my child? What the hell is wrong with this neighborhood? Maybe it's not just our house, perhaps this entire area is cursed.

Stephanie was playing with some of her new girlfriends in her bedroom, so I decided not to share this news with her yet. Jeff had come home earlier for a quick bite, then had to turn around and leave again. Before he left, he asked me to let him know what was going on as soon as I knew anything. He was running a crew at a new job downtown and wouldn't be home until much later. I hated nights like this when he wasn't home, especially when it was dark outside. I didn't mind too much being home alone during the daytime, even though it really didn't matter what time of the day it was. Weird things still happened. There was just something extra eerie about it being dark outside, I can't explain it. I hated being here alone at night. One of our neighbors is a widow who lives alone. I couldn't imagine living here alone, I just couldn't do it.

I called Jeff to tell him about the boy drowning in the lake when something strange happened . . .

"Jeff, can you hear me?"

I could barely hear him. He sounded like he was talking to me from miles and miles away, almost like he was talking through a tin can. It was the strangest thing.

I heard enough though to hear he was asking me to hang up and call him back.

I hung up the phone, waited a few seconds, then dialed him again.

"Jeff? Can you hear me now?"

"Yes, that's much better."

"What happened? Why couldn't you hear me?"

"All I could hear was some weird static on my end, then I heard some muffled whispering sounds, but couldn't make out what any of the words were. We must have just had a faulty connection because I can hear you fine now."

"Jeff, a boy whose family had just moved down the street drowned in the lake."

Jeff was silent on the other end of the phone. This was new to me, he's never been like this before.

"Jeff? You still there?"

"Yes, I just can't believe it. Our little man-made lake? How old was the boy who drowned?"

"He was only seventeen and considered the best swimmer on his high school's swim team."

"That's really odd and incredibly tragic."

"I know. I'm not letting Stephanie play down there anymore. At least not until we learn more about what happened to him."

"I'm sure that's wise, but don't expect Stephanie to be too thrilled about it. She loves playing down there."

"Well, at least she will still be around to be mad at me. I will take my chances and keep her alive."

I thought I heard Jeff laugh just then, but it didn't sound like his laugh either. It sounded more like a snicker than a laugh, and with a more sinister intent.

"Jeff, did you just laugh?"

"No, Julie, what would I be laughing about?"

"Did you hear it? Did you hear the laugh on your end? I heard a rather disturbing sound I can't quite describe, and I didn't think it sounded like you, either."

"Julie, relax, you've been through a lot today. Try to relax and I will be home as soon as I can."

Oh sure, I won't be relaxing until . . . Lord knows when.

"Please come home as soon as you can, you know I hate being here alone at night."'

"You're not alone, Stephanie is there."

"You know what I mean."

Click.

"Hello, Jeff? Are you still there? Hello?"

While I sat there waiting to hear Jeff's voice again, I heard the most disturbing and loud growl directly in my ear that sent my cell phone flying across the room. I freaked, jumped up and ran straight to Stephanie's room. I opened her closed door without even knocking first. I was panicking and needed to be around someone, anyone.

"Ma, what the heck? You're supposed to knock first."

"Sorry sweetie, I thought I heard you call me, is everything ok in here? Do you girls need anything?"

"Yeah Mom, it was fine until you busted in here."

"Ok, sorry I will leave you alone, but we will need to take your friend home soon."

Michelle piped up and said,

"My mom just called me and said she would come to get me soon."

"Oh ok, that's great, thanks, Michelle."

Secretly wishing her mom would like to stay and maybe even spend the night.

Problem is, how do I start that conversation?

Hey Angie, I'm afraid I might have something malevolent lurking inside my home. Want to spend the night?

I knew better than to invite a friend to spend the night without asking Stephanie first. I made that mistake once. I won't do it again. Plus, it's a school night, no mother is going to allow that on a school night. At least I'm relieved Stephanie is making new friends so we can have lots of sleepovers. *What was I thinking?* It's not a good idea to invite other children to our home, especially when I don't know what's going on. I don't even think it's safe for my own family to be here, let alone risk someone else's child. I really need to sort this out, which means I need to get some help.

∾

Where do I look? Paranormal exterminators? What do I search for? At least now there's the internet and I'm not stuck trying to find someone looking through the yellow pages. Good luck with that. I googled paranormal help and found a term I'd never heard before, "Paranormal Investigators." I searched for someone local and couldn't find anything. It's getting late so I will search more tomorrow. I'm relieved to know there are people who exist in the world who might be able to tell me what's going on. I haven't found anyone yet, but if they're out there, I will find them.

9

Today, I attended one of the saddest funerals I've ever been to. That's saying a lot because I've been to a lot of funerals for people who have died tragically. It surprises me how many people I've known who died in violent and terrifying ways. My good friend Pat from high school died in a horrible car accident. He was also seventeen, same age as the boy who drowned in the lake. He was driving home from the beach with five other friends in the car. He fell asleep at the wheel, hit the side of an overpass, and died instantly when the steering wheel hit him in the chest. The impact broke a rib which then punctured his heart. He died instantly. The friends who were in the car with him all survived, but barely. Some were in intensive care for months.

Three of my friends died in a bar shooting, and one of my closest friends died in the line of duty as a police officer. Her funeral will stay with me as the most incredible event I've ever been to. I'm sure it sounds strange to describe a funeral as an "event," but this one really was. First, it was huge. They held it in the armory building at the fairgrounds and it was packed full of people. The pageantry alone was breathtaking. Thinking about standing there watching so many police officers drive their motorcycles and patrol cars in honor of her still brings a tear to my eye. I remember standing outside watching the bagpipes play her favorite song and I thought to myself, "What a tribute, way to go, Maria." I hope I see nothing like this again, but I'm sure I will. Too much tragedy in our world not to, unfortunately.

I can't imagine what the boys' parents are going through today, and I pray I never have to know what it feels like to lose a child. Children are supposed to bury their parents, not the other way around. I fear his parents will never be the same. I didn't know them, but I felt compelled to attend the funeral today. My heart goes out to them. I was happy to see so many neighbors in attendance. This family needs all the support we can give them. I plan to take a casserole over to their house later today after the funeral. I don't know why, it's just what people do, I guess. It's what I always saw my grandma do after someone from her church died. Whether she knew them or not, she always brought a casserole to their grieving families' home. Classy touch, I thought, so I plan to do the same. If this funeral ever ends, I will. Catholic funerals, they never end. It's been a long time since I've been inside this church. I went to first grade in the school next to the church, and my memories of this place aren't exactly good. The church itself is really beautiful, but for me, it's cold and cruel. The dark confessional they used to make us sit in and confess our sins terrified me. I couldn't see the person in the room next to me to whom I was confessing, but in my young mind it might as well have been God himself. Every time I walked out of there alive was a win for me. I was considered evil by the nuns because I was born left-handed. They tried everything to break me, but in the end I conquered. I'm still a very strong lefty, and proud of it. Being different isn't a sin. But the nuns sure thought so. *Stupid bitches.*

The funeral finally ended. The coffin being carried by his friends, with the grieving parents walking behind it, slowly moving down the aisle toward the back of the church, was excruciatingly hard to watch. After they led every family member out, it was finally my turn to escape this dark cave of a place. The only good thing about being here were the gorgeous stained-glass windows. They were something to behold, and I stared at them through most of the funeral. At least this time I didn't get in trouble for daydreaming. What a relief to get out of here, I hope I never have to come back here again.

I hurried home to check on the casserole I had baking in the oven. I hope it's not burned. I didn't expect to be stuck in that funeral for two hours. I should have known better, but in my defense, it's been a really long time since I'd had to endure a Catholic funeral and the memory had faded from my mind.

Interesting how our minds protect us.

It was raining when we walked out of the church. I felt for the family having to stand outside in the rain at the cemetery. The rain is a metaphor for how we are all feeling today, especially his parents. The raindrops are the tears of his mother and father mourning the loss of their super star athlete and love of their lives. They must feel like the sun will never shine again. I know that's how I would feel. I can't imagine going on with life if I ever lost my daughter. One moment at a time until it's one day at a time, I've heard. I saw his mother's face as she walked down the aisle at the church. Our eyes connected for a moment and the sadness I saw in her eyes was indescribable. This woman was being tormented and I so desperately wanted to take her pain away. But how could I? The only thing that would help is to bring her son back. I've heard that God won't put anything on us we aren't capable of handling. This is one of those instances where I question that theory. Maybe God gives them extra strength during this horribly tough time to get through it all. I sure hope so, they're going to need it.

When I arrived home, I pulled the car inside the garage. The rain was pouring so hard I could barely see out the windshield while driving down our street. I almost had to pull over to wait until the storm passed, that's how hard it was coming down. Our long summer has just ended.

Thank God for electric garage door openers.

I walked inside the house and down the hallway into the kitchen when something on the floor in the living room caught my eye. I walked into the kitchen, sat my purse down on the counter, and grabbed an oven mitt to check my casserole. I'm afraid it's ruined. I opened the oven, pulled out the casserole and was relieved to see it wasn't. It was in better shape than I imagined. I sat the glass casserole dish on the top of the stove to cool a bit and went into the living room to see what, if anything, was on the floor. This is the most active room in the house, so I was feeling a bit nervous. Heaven knows what I might find, but nothing could have prepared me for what I did.

Lying on the floor was my Bible. It wasn't just lying on the floor either; it was lying flat on its back and wide open. As I stood there feeling a bit stunned, I realized it was much too far from the fireplace mantle to have fallen off on its own. Even if someone walked along and accidentally bumped it, it was still too far away from the mantle to have been an accident. This was deliberate, but why?

When I noticed things moving on the mantle, I placed my Bible there just in case. I thought if it were something malevolent, I might be able to calm it down with the presence of the Bible. *Couldn't hurt.* Now, it's laying open on the floor. I bent down next to it.

I took a closer look. I thought . . . if the Bible is lying open on the floor, perhaps there's a message on one of the pages I'm supposed to see.

There was.

I read the first page and nothing. When I got to the bottom of the second page, a familiar name caught my eye. I wasn't prepared for the shock I was in for. I saw, written on a page inside the Bible, my maiden name. I was stunned. Why in the world is my maiden name written anywhere, but especially written inside the most important book on the planet . . . *The Bible?* Again, how do I wrap my head around this?

I was so shocked I couldn't talk to anyone about it right away, but I knew I needed to talk to someone. I need to talk to my father first. Maybe he knows why our family name is written in the Bible.

After the shock wore off a little, I called my father.

"Hey Dad, do you have a minute? I need to talk to you about something."

"Sure sugar, what's up?"

"Dad, did you know your last name is written in the Bible?"

"No."

"Well, it is."

"Julie, don't joke with me, not about something like this."

"Dad, I swear, I'm not."

I didn't want to tell him exactly how I found out, so I just told him I was looking through the Bible and accidentally found it.

"That's amazing, what does it say about us?"

"Nothing, it's just mixed in with a bunch of other names."

"Show me next time we see each other."

"Alright, Dad, will do."

My father was a "prove it" kind of guy.

The following day, I took my Bible over to his house to prove it.

"Ok Peter, here you go."

"That's funny, Julie, real funny. By the way, it was Thomas who doubted Jesus, not Peter."

"Sorry, Dad, I thought it was Peter who doubted they crucified Jesus."

"Ever hear the saying, 'Doubting Thomas'? That's where it comes from."

Ugh, did I just go back in time and land in Catholic school?

"Here it is, Dad, here's the page our name is written on."

"I'll be damned."

For the first time, *most likely the first ever,* my father was at a total loss for words.

"That's amazing. By the way, Julie," Dad got closer and looked directly into my eyes, "how did you find this again?"

"Dad, you wouldn't believe me if I told you."

"Try me."

"Ok, but if I tell you, I can't un-tell you."

"Funny girl, just tell me already."

"Dad, I got home from the funeral to find the Bible laying open on the living room floor. It was open to the same page our name is written on."

"Incredible."

"Dad, I find it terrifying. Like who did this and how did they do it? I have a million questions with zero answers."

"Do you want me to call Father back?"

"Not yet, I don't know, I will let you know when I figure things out, ok?"

"Ok sugar, but always know your daddy is here for you."

"I know, Dad, I know."

Besides, how could it be an evil entity if it knows our name is written inside the Bible?

Crap! That's probably exactly what this is.

I hugged Dad goodbye and had no choice but to go back home. These days that task was getting harder and harder to accomplish. I was really starting to fear our home like I've feared no home before. It might sound crazy, but after what's happened so far, I'd almost give anything to go back to my old neighborhood, even if my bat shit crazy old fat piece of shit neighbor still lived there. And that . . . that is saying a lot.

I'm exhausted, I need to go home and try to get some rest. I'm not sleeping very well these days. I might try to get a nap in before it's time to pick Stephanie up from school. I got in my car and drove home, which wasn't far from my parents' house. They lived almost too close to us. I parked in the driveway, opened the garage door and went inside. So far, so good. Nothing major happening and it appears quiet to me today. It's weird how I'm learning how to sense when things are revving up. It's the same feeling as when I was a child. I used to sense when my mother was about to unleash her evil and do something crazy. For reasons unbeknownst to me, I usually knew what was about to happen before it happened. I sat down on the couch, turned on the television and leaned my head back.

The fun was just beginning. Everything I experienced until now *was nothing* compared to what was coming.

The real show is revving up and about to begin.

Everything before was just child's play. Just a little teaser, a suspenseful yet intentionally mild movie trailer leading up to what's coming next.

Are you ready to go?

What the hell? *Am I ready to go where?* Who was just talking to me? Oh man, I bet I fell asleep. I must be more tired than I realized. I have the strangest dreams when I'm exhausted. Thank God, it was just a dream. *Or was it?* Sometimes I have dreams that seem so real I can't tell what's reality and what isn't. Could it have been a warning? I'm sure it was just a creepy dream, let's not get it twisted, or get too hysterical. I can easily freak myself out, especially lately. It was just a dream, period. I've got to pull myself together or I'll be late picking Stephanie up from school. Oh, I know what it was. My mind was trying to wake me so I didn't forget to pick Stephanie up. That's where the "are you ready to go" part came from. Nice going, Julie, freak out over nothing. There's nothing strange going on in my home, it's all in my head. That's great, I'm going crazy, that's all. Paranormal stuff doesn't really exist, anyway. My father would say I'm just acting like a hysterical woman. Not real complimentary, but he's probably right. This can all be easily explained.

Too bad my logical mind was about to be crushed.

10

Summer is over and time is closing in on Thanksgiving. I was looking forward to hosting Thanksgiving dinner this year in my new home. I was relieved things were a lot calmer lately too. Stephanie was flourishing in her new school. They invited her to try out for their new volleyball team and made the cut. She's getting good grades, adjusting beautifully, and I couldn't be happier. I'm finally beginning to relax and really enjoy my new home. It's been a little over two weeks since the Bible landed on the floor.

I was returning home from dropping Stephanie off for their first early morning volleyball practice before school. I'm so proud of her, I can't wait to attend their games. Stephanie is very athletic. *I'm the polar opposite.* She also seems to be recovering well from the bullying she experienced at her old school . . . another reason we moved. I was being bullied by our next-door neighbor and Stephanie was being bullied by a little girl at school. Our move was necessary for many reasons.

I made a quick stop at our neighborhood 7-11 convenience store to pick up a few things. As soon as I walked in the door, I got a glimpse of my mean ole neighbor's husband standing across the room at the coffee machine. I turned to walk back out the door, *praying he didn't see me* when I heard his deep voice.

"Julie?"

I slowly turned around to see Dave standing in front of me.

"Oh, hello Dave, how are you?"

"Julie, I can't tell you how very sorry I am for what Donna put you through."

I almost collapsed onto the floor, I was in shock over what I was hearing. Did he just apologize for his wife?

"Hey, thanks Dave, I never blamed you for any of it."

"I know, Julie, but I'm very sorry for allowing it to carry on as long as it did because frankly, I just didn't want to get involved."

"I understand. Can I ask you a question? Do you live here now?"

"Yep, we moved about two weeks after you guys did."

"Why?"

"Well, what Donna never told you was we were only renting that house. The owners decided they were moving back to town, and they wanted their house back. We didn't have long to find another place, and selection was slim. A home became available not too far from here and we grabbed it."

Great, they live in my town now. At least they don't live in my neighborhood so there's that, but now I'm going to most likely have to see her stupid face at the grocery store. I can't stand even the sight of her.

I just wanted to get as far away as I could from that evil bitch. I still can't wrap my head around the fact that they live here now. Maybe I should start packing a gun.

Definitely not, I would shoot off my own foot.

Dave is such a nice guy. How the heck did he get wrapped up with someone like Donna? What could he possibly see in her? I guess the old saying really is true.

There really is someone for everyone.

Thanksgiving is tomorrow and I'm scrambling around to get everything ready for the fabulous dinner I planned to make. I'll just be happy if I don't kill anyone with my cooking. Cooking isn't what I excel in. My mother never taught me how to cook. Instead, she taught my brother. She said she didn't enjoy having me in "her" kitchen. That was fine with me, I didn't want to be around her, either. However, when it came time to do something simple like hard boil an egg, I had to swallow my pride and ask my husband if he knew how. He's a master at making the perfect hard-boiled eggs, so now it's his job. Fast-food restaurants and the microwave are my special helpers. Tomorrow however, I will be judged for everything I make because Dad and mommy dearest will be here. I also invited Jeff's parents over, his sister and her partner, and a friend of mine who doesn't have any family nearby. I didn't go to the trouble of making everything from scratch either. I tried that once. Now I just use boxed turkey dressing. It's way better than most homemade dressing I've ever had. Just bury the boxes in the garbage and nobody has to be the wiser.

I'm nervous about tomorrow.

I woke up the following morning around five o'clock feeling like I either had an intense case of the flu, or food poisoning. I was in terrible shape. I hadn't thrown up yet, but I was to the point of almost praying I could. Finally, around seven, I woke up just in time to run to the bathroom. I had it coming out of both ends. *Good times.* When you don't know what part to put on the toilet first, you know you're in hell. When Jeff woke up, I asked him if we should cancel the dinner. He didn't want to since it was Thanksgiving and we'd already invited everyone over. Jeff offered to make the dinner so I could stay in bed. I had no choice but to take him up on his offer. I was so sick and weak, yet I didn't feel right making everyone else suffer because of me. When it was time to put the turkey in the oven, I got up for a little while to help stuff it. As soon as we were done, I turned to go back to bed and was hit with the most intense pain. It felt like a hot metal rod had just impaled right through the middle of my chest in the soft spot under my rib cage.

I was in so much pain I doubled over and dropped to the floor.

"Oh yeah, I know what this is. Julie, you don't have the flu or food poisoning. You're having a pancreatitis flare-up."

"I agree, that's exactly what this feels like."

Two years ago, I had my first pancreatitis attack. I was in excruciating pain for over three months before the doctors figured out what was wrong with me. I had my gall bladder removed because they determined it was a gall stone that had landed on my pancreas and damaged it. I was on a feeding tube for over three months while allowing everything to heal. I sure hope I don't have to go back on a feeding tube again.

People mean well, but it's hard to go out in public with that tube coming out my nose. Pancreatitis is hands down the most painful thing I've ever experienced. Doctors have told me it's in the top five of the most painful illnesses a person can experience.

Now that I think about it, I've had a great deal of illnesses since we moved into this house. I was also in a hit-and-run car accident that could have easily killed me. I was told by the police officer I was very fortunate I wasn't killed instantly. Another car doing at least 55 mph broadsided my car.

The officer told me, "Most people die instantly when broadsided like you were, especially at such a high speed. The aorta can detach from the heart, and its instant death."

Shortly after the accident, a doctor diagnosed me with a disease called Fibromyalgia. The person who hit me is still on the loose. I also started having migraines again. I hadn't had a migraine in over ten years. Two weeks after we moved in, I had the most intense migraine I've ever had and it lasted for an entire week. The longest I ever had a migraine was three days. Migraines are headaches on steroids. Typically, with a migraine, I will lose vision in one eye and feel numbing in different areas on my face and hands. Occasionally, I will throw up. Vomiting is really fun when your head is exploding. This time I had all the symptoms which made it the worst migraine in the history of migraines. How does a person go ten years migraine free, then suddenly get struck down with the worst one ever? I was positive they were long gone.

Another issue I'm having is panic attacks. I haven't dealt with these either in a very long time. A week after we moved in, I started waking up to the most extreme panic attacks I've ever had. They've been bad, but never bad enough to wake me before. They were so intense I had to call an advice nurse to help me get through them. That was me, every single morning . . . calling the advice nurse, shaking so hard I could barely dial the phone. Each day the attacks grew more intense. I was sure I was about to die.

After two weeks they stopped happening in the morning and started happening at night right before bedtime. This time I was bothering my husband every night to help me through them instead of the nurse. One night my heart rate got well over 200 beats per minute. Jeff was less patient with me than the nurse. I guess since he's never experienced them, how could he know how bad they are. Honestly, I feel he just doesn't care about me that much anymore. It's strange, just another thing that's gone wrong since we moved in. Jeff had become more distant.

Finally, the panic attacks just stopped. I didn't understand why they started or why they left. Whatever the reason, I don't care; I was just glad to be rid of them.

So now, not only is the activity here freaking me out, I believe my house is also making me sick. I know Jeff will think I'm exaggerating and just being a hysterical woman, but deep down in my gut, I know there's something to it. I believe something strange is going on in my entire neighborhood, not just my house. I wonder if any other neighbors feel the same way. How would I ever know, I'm too chicken to ask.

Jeff did a wonderful job making Thanksgiving dinner, and the evening went off without a hitch. My father's only comment about me being sick was, "It's just nerves."

The following week they admitted me to the hospital for my "nerves." They inserted a feeding tube and gave me pain med through my IV. At least I wasn't in excruciating pain anymore and could finally sleep. This was an intense pancreatitis attack. They told me only ten percent of my pancreas was functioning. That terrified me. I didn't think I could survive without a pancreas so I was really convinced I was dying this time.

I believe strongly in the power of prayer, so I reached out to a large group of friends and asked for prayer. The most incredible thing happened after that. Only three days later the test results came back and the doctors told me they were even shocked my pancreas was functioning so well. They said it was now working well over fifty percent and they had no explanation for it.

I do, it's the power of prayer . . .

11

I t's been two weeks since they admitted me to the hospital. They scheduled me to be released within the next day or two when I began running a fever. The nurse gave me some Tylenol, and I fell asleep for the night. I woke up the following morning feeling extremely confused and not too sure where I was. Then I realized I was struggling to breathe. Jeff had just entered my room to find me in this condition. Through my haze, I could see it worried Jeff.

"Jeff, what's wrong with me? I'm really struggling to breathe and I'm soaking wet."

"I know Julie, do you know the last time a nurse was in here?"

"All I remember was a nurse coming in to give me some medicine last night around midnight."

"I'm going to strangle your nurse. She hasn't been taking care of you all morning until I got here. She took one look at you and called for help. She knows I'm pissed, and she knows you're in terrible shape. Don't worry, babe, people are coming to help."

All at once, a team of nurses and respiratory therapists came into my room carrying equipment I've never seen before. One of them pulled an x-ray machine into my room and they were setting up to take an x-ray of my lungs while I laid in the bed. Another nurse stood next to my bed. She was busy working on some equipment, yet close enough to hear my weak voice telling her I was scared.

"You're going to be alright, don't worry, we are going to take good care of you."

She held something over my mouth and then strapped it around the back of my head.

"Breathe deeply into this and try to relax. This will help you breathe."

Wow, she wasn't kidding. It really helped, except it made my heart beat so hard I thought it was going to explode. I was a mess. I thought I was dying . . . that, or I was in complete panic mode. Struggling this much to breathe is terrifying.

I remember this feeling. There was another time in my life when I came close to dying. That was when I had my out-of-body experience when I got sepsis from a kidney infection. This felt very similar, except I hadn't left my body, *yet*.

The x-ray showed I had double pneumonia. They put me on powerful antibiotics and I got the heart-beating-out-of-my-chest breathing treatments twice a day. This is the scary part about being admitted to the hospital. Come in with one problem and leave with two.

They finally got the pneumonia under control and they cleared me to go home. I still had the feeding tube in place, but I could manage that myself at home. I even got good at preparing the bags every night for feeding. It's very interesting how it works. It's a long tube they place in your small intestine, so it bypasses your stomach. The whole reason for feeding tubes is to let your pancreas rest. Then you take a bag that looks like an IV bag and fill it up with the liquid diet. Then I hooked the bag up to a standing hanger so it could drain the food into my stomach while I slept.

I really miss food.

Sucks to wear a feeding tube during the holidays. The best part about Christmas this year was watching Jeff kick my mother out of our house. Jeff and I may have been having some issues lately, but he always had my back where my mother was concerned. Stephanie even told him it was time to get Grandma out of here. Jeff loves telling that story to his male employees. He said they just chuckle under their breath.

On the other hand, my mother has never had my back and chose Christmas day to terrorize me. I was very surprised Jeff kicked her out, but it felt reassuring to know he still cared about me. Perhaps inviting my mother over to our home was a bad idea. She's such a mean, aggressive and negative person. I wonder if negative people attract negative energy, or even negative entities.

That might help explain what happened next.

It was two days after Christmas and I was home taking it easy. Nothing different about today from any other day. Until I get this feeding tube out, I really don't want to go anywhere in public. I'm lying around in my jammies being a total bum. At least I'm feeling almost back to normal and hopeful in a few days I can get this feeding tube removed. I had to get up to use the bathroom. Our bathroom is straight down the hallway at the very end. There's only one way in and one way out. As you walk into the bathroom, the sink is on the left, toilet next to the sink. Straight back is a bathtub. I was sitting on the toilet when something caught my eye outside the bathroom door. I sat there and starred in absolute horror.

To this day I don't know what it was I saw, all I can do is try my best to describe what it looked like. *There were two creatures.* I'm calling them "creatures" because they definitely didn't look human. They were tall black shadows meandering back and forth in front of the bathroom door. Their walk was very odd. They walked in a synchro-nized, rhythmic bouncing type of way. They were extremely tall, too. I couldn't see how tall they were because their heads were above the bathroom door and I wasn't getting up to look. They had abnormally long arms that appeared to drag on the ground. Nothing about this was normal. I sat there frozen to the toilet. What else could I do? The only way out was to run right through them. I was stuck inside the bathroom and feeling absolutely helpless. I didn't know what to do, so I prayed. I prayed to God, Saint Michael the Archangel, and anybody else who would listen. *Send all the angels my way, please.* I asked them to protect me and get these awful creatures out of my home. I reached out to God, and it worked. The creatures evaporated right before my eyes.

I was completely blown away by what I saw, yet not quite wanting to believe I actually saw it. It's a strange feeling. You know what you saw, yet understanding what it was is entirely different. That was definitely a "WTF" moment. What were those creatures? Why were they in my home? They didn't really pay any attention to me, they never turned their heads and looked at me, they were just walking back and forth as if guarding my door. I was watching them, but it was as if I wasn't even there. It was incredibly odd. They never made a sound either.

As I sat there in a total state of shock, I began to cry. I just sat there, crying my eyes out. I'm not sure what caused me to cry, but I know it was something I felt deep down in my soul. I don't even remember how long I sat there. After I got over the shock of it all, I stood up and ran out of there. Problem was, I'm out of the bathroom, but I'm still inside the house. I think I need to find somewhere to go for a while, just to clear my mind and get away from this house. I don't even care if I'm still wearing a feeding tube; I need to be around some people. I just need a break from the fear that anything can happen at any moment.

The question still lingers with me. What in God's name did I just see?

The cool part was, I asked for help and it came. Nothing quite compares to having the strength of God and the highest archangels on your side.

I drove to the nearest coffee shop, ordered a coffee and sat down. It was nice to get away. I can still drink liquids even though I have a feeding tube coming out my nose. I was feeling a little self-conscious, but it was better than being home. I saw one of my neighbors, but pretended I didn't notice her. I don't want to talk to anyone, I just want to sit and try to digest what just happened to me. Too late, she was on her way over to say hello.

"Hey Julie, how are you, or should I ask? When do you get that thing removed?"

"Hopefully next week."

"I heard from Maggie, you've really been through it, poor girl. Is everything finally on the mend now?"

"Yes, I'm recovering very well."

Ugh.

Then she asked me something that definitely got my interest.

"Julie, I don't really know how to ask you this and I hope you don't think I'm completely nuts . . ."

Now you're talking my language.

"Have you noticed anything strange going on in our neighborhood?"

I wanted to blurt out: *Yes, every single day in my house,* but instead I tried to play it cool.

"What do you mean?"

"Oh, I've just noticed a lot of neighbors coming and going and it seems odd to me. Our next-door neighbors were only living there for about a month before they moved. They put their house up for sale after they moved instead of living in it while they sold it."

"That's weird, Karen, I had the same thing happen with my neighbor. They left all their furniture behind. But what was strange is the fact that they even left their dinner dishes sitting on the table. Their landlord told me it looked like they just got up and left in the middle of dinner. I can't explain it, can you?"

"No, I can't."

Here comes the big question . . .

"Karen, do you mind if I ask . . . have you had any strange experiences in your home or anywhere in the neighborhood?"

"No, I haven't, but what kind of strange things are you talking about, Julie?"

"I don't know, maybe I have just heard the house settling, but sometimes I've heard some knocking sounds. Have you heard anything like that?"

"No, I haven't, it's probably just the house settling."

Karen looked a little uncomfortable and made some excuse about how she needed to go or she'd be late for a hair appointment.

Probably time for me to head home, I can't stay away forever. Even though I'm wishing I could more and more every day. I guess it's a bit of a mystery living here. I never know what's going to happen next. I hope I can figure it all out someday.

12

I pulled my car into the driveway and clicked on the garage door opener. I drove into the garage when something on the floor caught my eye. I left my car parked in the driveway, turned off the motor and got out. We have around twelve pairs of shoes we keep in the garage. They include yard shoes, play shoes for Stephanie, boots and sandals that are stored along a wall in the garage. Today, however, as I walk into the garage, I'm shocked to see all the shoes arranged in a perfect circle in the middle of the garage. *Not this again.* Not only are they arranged in a perfect circle, all the shoes are positioned inward and they are facing each other. This is the same exact thing that happened shortly after we moved here. I can't help but think someone broke into our garage and did this. Was this some kind of ritual or something? Is someone trying to scare us, or threaten us? I'm convinced an actual person had to have done this. I mean, moving objects is one thing, but positioning shoes in a perfect circle in the middle of our garage?

I go inside the house and as I'm walking down the hallway toward the kitchen, I sense I'm being watched. I feel like someone is standing directly behind me, so close they could almost breathe on my neck. I can feel the hairs stand up on the back of my neck. I'm getting angry,

I'm so tired and fed up with everything I just want whatever this is to leave us alone. I turn to leave the house again when I feel something punch me hard in the middle of my back. It hit me hard enough to knock me down on the floor, and I landed hard on my knees. "Stop it! Just fucking stop it!!"

I can't believe I just yelled at nothing.

Off in the distance came another sinister chuckle I've grown to recognize.

"Get out of my house."

Then it came, the thing I worried about the most. It wasn't a breath on my neck though, it was a growl directly inside my ear. I could feel the breath of whatever it was growling next to my ear.

I got up and ran out the back door into the garage. I was shocked to see the same shoes that were in a perfect circle only moments ago, were now thrown all over the garage. I didn't bother to stick around. I ran to my car and fled. I need help, this can't go on. Something inside my home is trying to kill me. I never had anything try to touch me before.

Stephanie was still at volleyball practice and Jeff was downtown starting a crew on a new building. Stephanie wasn't due home for another hour. At least I won't have to be home alone. I drove down to where Jeff was working so I could tell him about what had just happened. However, when I got to the new job, Jeff was pretty stressed out with the first day on the job issues and I didn't want to add to his stress. Besides, he probably wouldn't believe me, anyway. I'm not going home alone though, that's for sure. I decided to just drive around until Stephanie was due home.

I got home moments before Stephanie arrived. We sat out on the front porch, neither of us wanting to go inside. I was asking Stephanie how her practice went when she broke into tears.

"Baby girl, what's the matter?"

"Mama, I don't like our house. I had something happen last night, and I didn't know if I could tell you or not."

"Sweetie, of course you can tell me, you can tell me anything. You know I'm always here for you."

I don't feel at all prepared for what she might tell me, and I'm terrified something has tried to hurt her. However, I'm her mother, it's my number one job to keep my daughter safe.

"Please tell me, sweetie, tell mama what happened, it's ok, I want to know."

"OK, well you know my purple princess phone, the one that stands on my table near my bed?"

"Yes?"

"Well, last night I could hear it lift a little off the thing it sits on."

"I think that's called a phone cradle."

"Anyway, I could hear people talking inside my phone, but I couldn't hear what they were saying. So, I picked up the phone and I could still hear lots of people talking inside my phone, but I couldn't understand what any of them were talking about. Then there was this loud static sound, and I dropped my phone on the ground."

Jesus.

"That's really strange, honey, did anything else happen?"

I'm barely keeping my composure, but I don't want to scare her any more than she already is, so I'm trying my best to stay calm.

"Yes, I hear scratching sounds on my walls and it sounds like something is hitting the washing machine. Sometimes it sounds like the door on the dryer opens and shuts repeatedly."

The washing machine is in the utility room which sits on the other side of her bedroom wall and directly next to the wall is her bed.

"Tell you what pumpkin, why don't we go move your bed to the other wall for tonight, does that sound like a plan? Also, let's take that phone out at night so it can't bother you, alright?"

"Mama, what's the matter with our house? I feel like I'm being watched all the time, and I think I even saw a little girl running down our hallway. I know that sounds crazy since I'm the only little girl who lives here, but I know I saw a little girl."

"Sweetie, when did you see this little girl?"

"I think it was the day before yesterday. She was just running and kind of skipping down the hall, and she didn't even notice I was there."

"Babe, did you see where she went?"

"Yep, she ran into the coat closet. Mama, she ran right straight through the closet door. The closet door wasn't even open, and she ran right through it. How did she do that?"

"I don't know, baby, but I know that I'm going to sort this out. I don't want you to worry. Ok? Mama and Jeff are always here to keep you safe. Also, whenever you get scared all you need to do is say your prayers and ask God to protect you, alright peanut?"

"Ok, mama, I will."

Whoever, or whatever you are, you better run. It's one thing to terrorize me, but now you're scaring my child? I'm telling you now, you leave my child the hell alone. You're not touching my child. I'm going to obliterate you.

I got Stephanie's room rearranged and finally talked her into going to bed. I bought her an angel night light for added assurance and she finally drifted off to sleep. I stayed with her until she fell asleep and took her phone with me when I left. Poor baby, she doesn't deserve this. I don't care how tired Jeff is when he gets home tonight; we are going to have that talk. This stupid dream house of ours has turned into my worst nightmare. All I care about is keeping my daughter safe. Now more than ever, I want to move. It might be beyond just a desire to move. What if it isn't safe to stay?

That's it, that's the angle I will use when I talk to him.

Jeff didn't get home until after midnight. I had fallen asleep on the couch waiting for him to come home. He was tired and cranky, so I waited another day before I lowered the boom on him. Plus, he will be much more receptive in the morning. *I hope.*

After I took Stephanie to school, I came back home and waited for Jeff to wake up. Finally, he came into the front room ready for his breakfast. I waited until he finished eating before I talked to him. Men do much better on a full stomach.

"Jeff, we need to talk."

He had a look of "what now" on his face.

"Jeff, I want to move."

"Not this again. Julie, you know we can't afford to move, all our savings, everything is tied up in this house. Where would we even go? I guess something else 'paranormal' happened?"

"Yes, as a matter of fact, something else did happen. I'd appreciate it if you didn't use that mocking tone of voice with me."

"Sorry, I just woke up, I really didn't mean to sound so rude. Let's start over, tell me what's going on."

"Jeff, living here has become hell on earth."

Out of nowhere, Jeff laughed. It startled me because it felt so awkward and inappropriate, yet strangely terrifying. Then he looked at me in a way he's never looked at me before. It made me uncomfortable but even worse; it made me fear my husband.

"You do not understand. It's just the beginning, sweetheart."

"What? What did you just say?"

"Relax, I said nothing."

"Jeff, you said . . ."

"Julie, I really can't discuss this right now. I have an important meeting and I don't want to be late."

"Alright."

Hey babe, there's something here that's trying to suck the life out of me, but by all means, don't be late for your precious meeting.

The scariest part is, I think Jeff wasn't lying when he said he doesn't remember saying anything. What just happened to Jeff? It felt to me as if something took over his body for a short period and talked through him. This is crazy, that only happens in scary movies, not real life. How is it even possible? I need to stop thinking crazy thoughts. I doubt there's any hope we can move, however, I definitely need some more help. I believe Father Rainey helped for a short period, but whatever was here before is back. I fear it came back with a vengeance.

What should I do now? Go talk to a different priest? We already tried with the most experienced priest in town, how is another priest going to do anything different? Besides, I'm afraid to bring in another priest. I fear bringing another priest into our home could even make things worse. I need to try something else.

I searched online for paranormal investigators in our area. I was extremely surprised how much information I found. It gave me an odd sense of peace. For so long, I've felt so alone. Maybe there really are others out there in the world who struggle with this too. I definitely need to reach out to these people. I picked a local team and sent them an email explaining what was going on. I felt so hopeful when I hit the send button. For the first time I have hope that just maybe . . . maybe soon, someone will help us.

There's got to be help out there. Why else would there be so many paranormal investigators? Makes me think there's a lot more going on in my town than even I realized. This entire town could be haunted, I'm sure my entire neighborhood is. Well, maybe not totally sure, but I have a good idea it is. If my intuition is correct, it's cursed.

13

I just saw the little girl. The little spirit girl Stephanie has been telling me about. It was around one in the afternoon. I was sitting on the couch, knitting a blanket and watching an afternoon talk show when I thought I heard a giggle. It sounded like it was coming from down the hall.

I'm alone in the house, so I'm telling myself if I heard anything it had to have come from outside. This didn't sound like it was coming from anywhere outside though, and deep down I knew it was coming from inside. I got up to walk down the hall when I saw a flash of light coming straight out of the coat closet, as if a rocket had just propelled itself through the closed closet doors. I stood there in absolute awe, yet I remained strangely calm. I didn't feel any fear this time as I had in the past. Instead, I felt intensely curious. I had a feeling it was the little girl Stephanie told me about and I definitely wanted to see her. As soon as that thought popped into my head, I saw her.

She was a young girl. I'd estimate her age to be somewhere between eight and eleven. She was wearing a red plaid dress. Her hair was pulled back in a ponytail with a fabric bow that matched her dress. She had long brown curly hair. She skipped out of the closet and down the hallway before she completely disappeared. She was there one moment and gone the next. She disappeared as if she were vapor. I saw her full-bodied, not even see-through, and when she disappeared, her body morphed into a mist before she was gone. She seemed to be a very happy little girl and wasn't at all aware of my presence. It felt like I was watching her from another dimension and she couldn't care less about me being there. Right after she disappeared, I saw a big white ball fly out of the coat closet. It hovered so close to me . . . I swear I just saw something inside it.

I think I just saw an orb with the little girl's face inside of it.

At the same moment, Stephanie's dog, Lilly, began barking. Lilly was standing there stiff as a board, staring at the coat closet. I've seen Lilly do this frequently, but today her bark was louder and more aggressive. It sounded like a threatening bark. It really startled me. Lilly barks a lot. But this time was different. It was like hearing her bark snapped me out of some type of a trance or something. It scared the crap out of me, so I yelled at Lilly to stop barking, but Lilly never listened to me. I yelled even louder at her to stop barking and again she completely ignored me. Lilly's barks grew more intense, and she snarled at something I couldn't see.

It's hard to explain this, but another voice seemed to come out of nowhere. I could hear Stephanie's voice, but this time in a very grown up authoritative manner.

"Lilly! Shut up!"

With that, Lilly stopped barking, ran away from the closet and slid under the chair to hide. I've never seen Lilly that scared before.

How the hell did that just happen? Stephanie was still at school. She's not even here, and yet I clearly heard her voice yelling at Lilly to stop barking. More astounding than that was the fact that Lilly heard it too and stopped barking. Lilly doesn't listen to me. She only listens to Stephanie. Whatever commanded Lilly to stop barking knew it would work. The scariest part about all this is the fact that something here can mimic our voices, and that scares the hell out of me. I wonder if human spirits can mimic people's voices. *I've heard demons can.* That doesn't give me any kind of peace of mind, especially since I'm already convinced something evil is inside our home.

I haven't heard from the paranormal investigators I emailed yet. It's only been a few days, but I need help now. Back to the drawing board, I guess. This time I won't tell them too much about my house. Maybe I scared them away. I've never dealt with anything like this before, so I really don't know what I'm doing. I know one thing for sure. I need to get out of this house for a while and go somewhere I can relax. I'm always so anxious inside the house these days.

I was walking down the hallway toward the back door to go into the garage where my car's parked. I'm especially scared walking down the hall lately. So much activity coming from the hallway and especially the front room these days. We're still hearing banging sounds in the hallway; very reminiscent of the knocking sounds I heard when I was hanging pictures, only these are louder. Footsteps like heavy clomp, clomp, clomp boot sounds that end up being nobody. It feels like someone *or something* is desperate to get my attention.

I feel it's becoming even more urgent to get some help in here. Most of the time I just want to pack up and move like our neighbors did, but then there's the question of how could I, in good faith, sell this to some unsuspecting person? I strongly feel I need to figure out what's going on and get rid of it so nobody else has to deal with it like we have. It just wouldn't feel right to put this on someone else. I'm going to go to the coffee shop and do another search for help.

I was at the end of the hallway about to walk into the laundry room when I felt a cold, *no* it was an icy cold breeze blowing directly across my face. This was such an icy breeze that went from my face down throughout my entire body. It made me feel frozen in space as I was attempting to take my next step. I looked down at my foot in amazement to see it suspended in midair. I was about to set my foot down on the ground to take the next step, but it had become instantly so frozen in place I couldn't move it. It felt like something was holding my foot and not letting me move any further. I tried as hard as I could to push my foot down to the ground and it wouldn't budge. I'm suspended there, frozen in the middle of my next step. It was the strangest experience I've ever had in this house. *No, it's the strangest thing I've ever expe-*

rienced in my entire life. How in the world do I explain what's going on to myself, let alone another person? I can't believe what's happening, how do I expect anyone else to believe me?

The most wretched smell just blew across my face. Again, feeling panicked, I tried with everything I had to move, but I just couldn't. There was a force here that was too strong for me, and I never felt more fear than at this very moment. The smell emanating through the air and moving across my face was that of rotting flesh. I closed my eyes and tried to make it go away. I wasn't seeing anything terrifying this time; it was keeping me frozen in place and invading my senses. The smell was horrible. My leg is hurting from the position it's stuck in. It feels like the muscle around my calf is cramping, but I think something is tightening its grip around me to hold me there and it's making it feel like a painful Charlie horse. I can feel icy stiff fingers wrapping around my leg and digging sharp fingernails into my skin. I need help and I need it now.

At the exact moment I panicked, a thought came to me. The thought that popped into my brain was more like a message. What I mean is, it didn't feel like the thought was my own, but more like some kind of assurance; some kind of help from another realm telling me how to get out of my predicament. It felt like something was being downloaded into my brain and the message was . . . *pray.*

The only prayer I could think of was the "Our Father." However, that's not the prayer that came out of my mouth that day. As I stood there frozen, about to take my next step and wondering if I were going to live or die, the prayer that came out of my mouth instead was "Saint Michael the Archangel" prayer. I didn't even know this prayer. I've heard it in church before, but by no means did I have any of it memorized. I didn't even know the first line of the prayer, but there I was, reciting the prayer like it was a prayer I'd learned long ago.

Saint Michael, the Archangel,
defend us in battle.
Be our protection against the wickedness and snares of the devil;
May God rebuke him, we humbly pray;
And do thou, O Prince of the Heavenly Host,

by the power of God,
thrust into hell Satan and all evil spirits
who wander through the world for the ruin of souls

I recited this prayer over and over, and as I said the prayer, my voice grew stronger and louder. As I continued saying the prayer, I was able to gain strength and some kind of hidden power from within myself to shield me from my fears. I finally began feeling empowered and at that moment whatever had a grip on me let me go with such force it knocked me into the wall. I didn't care; I was finally free. Saint Michael, and all his heavenly hosts of warrior angels came to my rescue that day as I stood there all alone. I knew beyond a doubt . . . I was in the presence of angels.

As a child I attended Catholic school for six very long torturous years. I remember hearing this prayer in church, but I wasn't familiar enough with it to recite it the way I just did. Even though I hated Catholic school, *the nuns terrified me,* and I hated how they treated me, *I refer to myself as a "recovering Catholic"* I still have a strong faith in God. There's no doubt in my mind I had some extra help today from a divine source. What other explanation could there be? Something diabolical is definitely in our home and now I believe it's trying to hurt me. No doubt about it.

I think it's time I go back to the church and request an exorcism instead of asking a paranormal group to come poke around. I know what I have to do now.

I need divine intervention, and I need it fast.

14

The last thing I ever wanted to do was step foot back inside a Catholic church. Especially the one downtown where I was tortured in the first and second grade. I went to all the other Catholic churches in town first and nobody would help me. I had no choice but to go back to where my horror began. At least this time an actual priest agreed to talk with me. Maybe things are looking up.

Sure thing.

I really should have known better than to get my hopes up. I couldn't believe what I was hearing.

"I'm sorry Julie, demons don't exist and neither do spirits."

"Forgive me, Father, but yes they do. I've seen both with my own eyes."

"We don't believe in such things, there's usually some logical explanation for those things that go bump in the night."

"Can you please just come out to our home and bless it again? Maybe if you come visit my house, you will understand what I'm talking about."

"No, if it didn't work the first time, what makes you think it will work a second?"

"Father, with all due respect, I'm desperate. My family isn't safe, something diabolical is in my home. You're my last hope, please help me."

"I can't help you, but I can offer to give you some holy water and blessed salt. Maybe having that in your house will make you feel better. If you fear something is going on, you can spray holy water around the house and lay salt at your doors and windowsills."

Funny, he doesn't believe in ghosts, but he's offering me holy water and blessed salt. My personal feeling is, he's too damn afraid to come to my home.

I pleaded with him again, but to no avail. He recommended I see a counselor instead. I never felt more offended. He thinks I'm crazy. Aside from that, the feeling I'm experiencing the most is shock. This feels so strange to me. I always thought priests believed in heaven and hell, which means they should believe in demons, too. I mean, if they believe in angels, then why not demons? It's my understanding that Satan was a fallen angel. Here's a priest sitting in front of me, looking me directly in the eye, telling me he doesn't believe in demons. Wait a minute . . . aren't exorcisms usually performed by sanctioned Catholic priests? That was always my understanding. Maybe that's only true in the movies.

The only option I had now was to accept what he was willing to give me. He gave me a bottle full of holy water and poured a small amount of salt into an envelope. At least it was a legal-sized envelope. As I walked out of his office, I felt more defeated than ever before. I'm all alone to battle whatever evil forces decide to terrorize me and my family. I'm also feeling some old familiar feelings of being dismissed and abandoned by this priest. The church was never kind to me when I was a child. Why should today be any different? My anger toward them was coming back to the surface and only grew over time.

I left his office and walked down the stairs out to my car. When I got inside my car, the tears started to flow. It was so strange, I cried as if I were mourning a loss. I feel so alone, but worse, I feel betrayed and dismissed. I know this feeling all too well. My sadness will turn to anger soon enough, I know that much about myself. However, I have a bigger problem to deal with and I really don't have anyone to turn to.

Now what the hell do I do?

~

Foremost, I need to forget what happened with that idiot priest and pull myself together. My family needs me to be strong, especially now. I began feeling more determined than ever before. I rarely have a lot of confidence in myself, but now's the time to find some. I drove to the nearest Christian bookstore to arm myself with as many blessed items as I could find. If I have to fight this alone, I'm going in prepared. I purchased about ten blessed crosses, and thirty blessed medals to place around our home. I hung a blessed cross above every door and placed the blessed medals inside window sills and above door jams. I purchased a laminated card with the Saint Michael prayer on it since I really didn't have it memorized. I sprayed holy water in every room while I said the prayer to Saint Michael. I also went outside and poured the blessed salt around the front, back and sides of our house. I also purchased some blessed oil and made the sign of the cross above every door. This took all afternoon to accomplish, but I was feeling stronger and more prepared to take on whatever might be coming my way. I was feeling more confident than ever before, but more importantly, I was feeling empowered.

I'm impressed, it really seems to work. The house has never felt better, the sun is shining through the windows and best of all, it smells fresh. I swear I even heard the birds chirping outside, and I hadn't heard that sound in months, quite possibly the first time ever since we moved here. I went back to life as normal and really enjoyed our new home. I even believed as long as I had holy water and blessed salt that I had the power to keep us all safe.

Couldn't have been further from the truth.

It was day sixteen of my cleanse. The most "activity free" days since we moved in. It was getting dark outside, so I was going about my nightly chore of closing window blinds. I was feeling very proud of myself and happy to be free of whatever had been terrorizing us. But most of all, I was feeling a sense of empowerment like never before. I felt like a warrior ready to face anything. I was free for the first time in a very long time. I was finally happy, content and peaceful in my beautiful new home.

Too bad that was short-lived . . .

I was in the middle of closing our bedroom blinds when I felt something grab me from behind and yank me backward. It was so forceful I'm not sure how I managed not to fall. It kept pushing on me, trying to push me down when I heard a loud growl directly in my ear. I was frozen in fear. *Let me go, don't hurt me, don't hurt me, don't hurt me.* I started screaming and freaking out, without realizing it was all inside my head. Finally, when I could get some sound out, I yelled, "let me go" and it loosened its grip. I ran out of the room crying hysterically. I didn't have any shoes on, but fortunately, I still had my car keys in my pants pocket. I fled the house. I left with no purse, no driver's license, no money and no shoes on my feet. I had nowhere to go. I just drove around until I felt brave enough to go back.

Who am I fooling? So much for feeling empowered. I know I'm never going to have that wonderful feeling back again. But what are my choices? I can't abandon my family and keep driving around in circles without a clue in the world what to do. I'm heading back to hell, it's the only option I have. I just wanted to put my car on the freeway and keep driving to anywhere. I feel like a prisoner in my own home. A prisoner in life.

I need to pull myself back together. My family needs me. I might be the only one to put an end to all of this, *whatever this is*, once and for all. Deep down, I really didn't believe I could do anything to help me or my family. I didn't know where to turn and my confidence just shattered all over the place in no time at all. The priest won't come to our home, he won't lift a finger to help us. It's all on me and nobody is coming to help. My dream home is back to being my house of horrors. I was safer in the dump I used to live in. *Much safer.* I've wanted to sell our new home so badly, but my conscious won't allow me to sell this nightmare to another unsuspecting family. I just can't do that. I'd love to burn it to the ground, though. Whatever evil is here just showed me who's in charge.

My battle continues . . .

15

F ear can be a terrible thing, or it can motivate you. Fear can also give spirits or other entities more energy. I learned that lesson the hard way. For me, all the fear and anxiety I've been experiencing lately has given me night terrors. That is, when or if I'm able to fall asleep. I was experiencing anxiety on a whole new level and let me tell you, it was constant. I've had anxiety disorder since the age of twenty-one. I will never forget my first panic attack. This was like anxiety on steroids.

Be careful what you wish for and even more cautious with your own thoughts. Some evil entities can read your mind and use that to control you. Sometimes our thoughts aren't our own. Evil entities can place thoughts inside our minds. If you are thinking of something, then you hear a voice responding to what you're thinking of, that's your proof. I was thinking about the reality of what I've experienced so far when off in the distance I heard a voice say . . .

"Sometimes monsters are real."

I desperately wanted to figure out what was happening inside our home, but even more terrified that I would. There's an old saying, "The more energy you give a malevolent spirit, the stronger it gets." This isn't just a saying, it's a fact. I want to believe, but I also don't. What I can conjure inside my brain is far more terrifying than anything I've seen. I just dread the day when, or if, it comes to life. Are our minds strong enough to conjure into reality what we fear? In my experience, I believe it's possible. Sometimes things happen to people that there just isn't an explanation for.

I believe our subconscious mind can be a portal for the spirit world. When you're asleep and dreaming your subconscious opens up. Dreams can act as portals, like a bridge from one dimension to another. It's the most optimal time for something supernatural to come in and make contact. I've experienced this myself many times. But my question is . . . can the portal I open up in a dream state also act as a portal for whatever I'm dreaming about to come into my reality? More importantly, can I dream the scary monster into real life? Creatures from our nightmares can present themselves any way they want. If they appear in your dreams? Can they appear in your waking life and manipulate the environment? For me personally, I think it's possible. We are so vulnerable when we're asleep.

It's never happened to me before we moved into this house. I mean, I really treasure the dream visits I've had from my grandma. I even saw Jeff's father transition into the afterlife here. There are times, *in my dreams* I leave my body and fly around the city. I always go to this one intersection in the middle of downtown and hover there, peacefully watching cars go by. It's a fun, yet weird thing to experience. I'd like to say I have some control over it, but the truth is, I don't. It just happens. I have what I consider to be out-of-body experiences in my sleep, and I always fly around downtown. It's incredibly relaxing and peaceful. I love these dreams because I feel such incredible freedom. I've often wondered if I fly in this dimension or if I go into the astral plane. I've been told it's possible to fly into the astral plane in our sleep. If it's true, then I know the astral plane looks very similar to our world. There are cars and buildings in the astral plane. If, in fact, I've been there.

However, the night terrors I've been having lately are on a whole new level. I've experienced nothing as horrific as these.

I hate to admit it, but there are things in my past I never shared with Jeff before we married. Not because it's some big secret, I just didn't want him to think I was crazy. I didn't know how to tell him I left my body and almost touched the veil between our world and the next. He knows I almost died when I was fifteen, but he doesn't know the whole story.

~

Since the age of two, I suffered from painful kidney infections. I was told someday I'd need a kidney transplant. When I was fifteen, I had another one of my kidney infections, except this time I was sicker than usual. I remember lying on the couch in excruciating pain while my mother sat in the chair next to me, talking on the phone and smoking one cigarette after another. When I begged her to stop smoking because it was making me nauseous, she just waved her hand at me and kept smoking and talking on the phone.

She never gave a shit about me.

When my father finally came home from work it was after nine o'clock in the evening. He walked in the door just in time to hear me pass out in the bathroom. He ran to our neighbor doctor for help, but unfortunately the neighborhood doc he went to was an eye doctor. He still came over with my father to check on me. Together they revived me and helped me onto the couch.

"Bud, you really need to call her regular physician. She doesn't look good."

My doctor at the time was Doctor Bright. I thought he was the smartest and kindest man on the planet.

"Bring her to the emergency room. I will be there when you arrive."

Finally, I might have a chance. No thanks to my stupid mom.

The second we arrived at the hospital a large group of nurses ran outside. They lifted me out of the car and laid me on a gurney. I was too weak to walk. They pushed the gurney as fast as they could through the double doors and into the hospital. I don't remember much, but I do remember how fast they rushed me inside. I was pretty out of it by the time I got to the trauma room. However, I remember the exact moment I left my body.

I glided out of my body with surprising ease. I was free from pain and bathed in the most incredible radiant warmth. I floated up to the corner of the room and hovered there. I could feel my body slowly rise and fall as I floated in midair.

It was incredibly cool.

I looked down and was a little surprised when I realized I was looking down at myself lying unconscious on a hospital bed, but I couldn't have cared less. I loved the fact that I wasn't in pain anymore, and that's really all I cared about. I wasn't aware that I was dying, nor was I the least bit afraid. I was merely an observer hovering in the corner, and nobody knew I was there. I saw a nurse run in the room pushing something they referred to as a "crash cart." Then I heard another nurse say, "Doctor, we're losing her." Still, it really had no impact on whether I cared, I was enjoying the feeling of pain-free freedom. It was like not having a care in the world for the very first time. That's the best way I can describe it.

Then, without warning, I felt two enormous hands pushing me back inside my body. The force was intense, and beyond anything I've ever felt before. I had no choice, I was going back into a body racked with pain. As soon as I became conscious again, I screamed out in pain. A nurse gave me a shot that was almost as good as being up in the corner. At least it took most of my pain away and I could finally speak.

"I was up in the corner watching you."

"No dear, you're just hallucinating."

I'm so offended.

I told the nursed what I saw while hovering in the corner.

"OK, first you," *as I pointed to the first nurse* "ran out of the room to get what you called a crash cart."

Then I pointed at the nurse standing next to her.

"You told the doctor that you were losing me."

They just looked at me with their mouths dropped.

"Well? Am I right?"

"Yes, but how could you have known? You were unconscious the whole time."

"No, I wasn't, I was up in the corner like I said. I saw everything that happened until some jerk pushed me back inside my body."

I saw one nurse make the sign of the cross after my last comment. I think she might have actually believed me. The rest of them? Not a chance.

The weirdest part about this experience was. . . when I left my body, so did my illness. After being in the trauma room for a little over an hour, they sent me home. I made a full recovery the following day, and I never had another kidney infection since. I'm the lucky recipient of a miracle with an incredible story to tell.

My out-of-body experience came with some unexpected side effects. I saw my first spirit a year later. It was a Civil War soldier standing proudly across the room from me. I was alone in our living room listening to music when he appeared. Based on his uniform, he was a union soldier, I just didn't know it yet. I found out after I researched his uniform. I found it odd a Civil War soldier came to me when I don't live anywhere near where any Civil War battles were fought. I live in Oregon. What I believe happened is, when I left my body, I came close to the veil between our world and the next. Perhaps I came back with some abilities I might not have had otherwise.

I really should have told Jeff about this. It wasn't really that big of an issue for me since the age of sixteen. I was so freaked out by it, I somehow managed to shut it all down. I couldn't risk my friends knowing I was different, so I stopped it from happening. I'm not sure how, but I did. I even had a teacher in high school point out to the entire classroom that I could see auras. *It traumatized me.* My friends started looking at me differently, and I had to make the teacher out to be a total nut. I couldn't risk losing my friends. Since I had such a horribly abusive mother, my friends were what I called my love supply. I desperately needed them to accept me. I shut my abilities down for many years. I mean, most of my abilities. I couldn't really do anything about my dreams. Those abilities stayed with me and spirits frequently visit me in my dreams. But only the loving and nice ones like my grandma Eva. She usually came to me when I needed her the most. She visited me in a dream when I was brutally raped in college and almost killed. When I was at the end of my rope, my grandma always appeared to me.

This was my first spirit visit from my grandma. I woke up when the front doorbell rang, or so I thought. I got out of bed and suddenly . . . I was outside my body watching myself walking down the stairs and toward the front door. The moment I put my hand on the door handle, I was back inside my body again, but this time, I wasn't in any pain.

Grandma was standing at my front door and the first thing she said to me was, "Julie, take my hand." I instantly felt her hand in mine. Grandma Eva and I took a long walk together through the streets of my dark neighborhood. The whole time she reassured me I was going to be alright. I know Grandma was really there, I know it was a spirit visit. How do I know? I dreamed about her in the same clothes she was buried in, right down to the crystal brooch she wore. I described her attire perfectly to my father one day, and he turned completely white. He told me they buried her in that blue suit along with her crystal brooch and black patent leather high heels. This is exactly the way Grandma always appears to me.

She died when I was six. I wasn't allowed to attend her funeral. I have no memory of ever being told what they buried her in. Is that really something you share with a six-year-old? Perhaps some would, but I guarantee my parents wouldn't. It left me with my spiritual dreams, no longer seeing spirits in real life.

Until we moved into this house . . .

Now my dream state is like a portal for whatever I'm dreaming about to come into my reality. I still feel like I'm in the middle of the nightmare, yet I'm awake. Mostly when I'm having a nightmare, I have this uncanny ability to reassure myself inside my dream that it's not real, it's only a dream. Usually it happens like this . . . I see myself off in the distance. I look over and I hear my voice say, "It's not real, it's just a dream." If the dream is scary or dangerous, I can wake myself up. Usually I'm drenched in sweat, but at least I'm awake and away from the terror.

I recently had a night terror when I didn't reassure myself inside the dream it was only a dream. It felt real and was very vivid, just like the dreams I've had with my grandma. Something evil was after me and I couldn't move. My legs froze, and my feet felt like they were glued to the floor. I tried to scream for help, but no sound came out. I tried to reach for my phone when I could finally move my arm and as soon as I touched it, it flew into the wall and shattered. I was running down the hallway when I finally woke up. I've never had this happen to me before. I've never woken from a bad dream anywhere other than my bed. I didn't go back to sleep that night. Most nights these days I'm terrified to fall asleep.

The most intense night terror I've ever had still haunts me to this day. I thought I had woken up, yet I couldn't move. It paralyzed me. It still felt like I was in the middle of the nightmare, yet still completely convinced I was awake. Instead of waking me, my dream started warning me. Something dark and ancient was trying to kill me.

Suddenly, this thing starting crawling up my bed toward me. It had the body of a human and the head of a lizard with bright green neon eyes. I've never seen a color so bright, and I will never forget how those eyes pierced through me. It definitely wasn't human. I just didn't know what it was. But I knew what it wasn't. It wasn't good. I believe it was a demon. Demonic entities are notorious for shape shifting and mimicking. The next night I had the same dream yet was awake, and this time the creature looked like a gargoyle with alligator skin. Every night for two weeks it was there. I tried to convince myself it was just a nightmare. It started out as a nightmare, but somehow materialized into reality. I began waking up with bruises and scratches. I started sleeping on the couch with my grandma's rosary beads. Luckily, the creature stopped bothering me. As long as I had my grandma's rosary beads in my hand, I was safe.

∾

To know your worst nightmare can manifest into reality is terrifying and overwhelming. I still haven't coped with it. I have come face to face with pure evil. I believe now that demons and other creatures we aren't even aware of can take on all forms and look like nothing we've ever seen before,. and nothing you could ever imagine. This thing . . . it could read my mind. It knew my fears, it knew my every desire, and I knew it's intent. It wanted to destroy me.

Sometimes your worst fears can become reality.

16

Life was moving along a little better now that I sleep on the couch every night with grandma Eva's rosary. I'm grateful she was such a religious lady. She walked over three miles every day, rain or shine, to attend early mass at Saint Joe's. I'm sure her priest blessed her rosary many times. I know it's the only thing keeping me safe at night, and it gives me the ability to feel comfortable enough to fall asleep. That's huge for me since before I tried using her rosary, I was incredibly sleep deprived. I keep the television and the kitchen light on all night, too. I need additional sounds to keep from hearing anything paranormal.

Jeff and I are even getting along better. I'm a little nervous because everything seems to be going almost too well. Historically, when things are moving smoothly in my life, something horrible usually happens. Not to be a drama queen, it's just a fact. I'm always a little more careful when life is going too smoothly for me. This usually means something terrible is about to happen.

And something evil was indeed coming my way . . .

I was taking a shower the following morning. I had just stepped into the shower when I heard a whistle. A man was whistling at me the way a construction worker whistles at a sexy girl walking down the street. Only problem was, I'm in the shower, not walking down the street, and I'm the only one in the house. This is usually when this crap happens to me, when I'm alone and vulnerable. I felt someone grab my arm, then a sharp stabbing sensation hit me in the middle of my back. It was so intense I fell to the floor, and as I scrambled to get a grip on the door handle, something was grabbing at my feet as if they were trying to pull me down the shower drain. I immediately prayed. Instead of trying to fight whatever was there, my instinct told me to just pray. As soon as I prayed the "Our Father" prayer, everything stopped, even the intense pain I was feeling in my back. I stood up, opened the shower door and ran out of there. I haven't been able to use this shower since. I performed a cleansing ritual as soon as I got dressed.

~

Another month of peace went by. Nothing, not even a ghost sighting, but I began sensing something was here. It felt like I was being constantly watched. It's that feeling that makes you look over your shoulder expecting to see someone standing there, but nobody is ever there. *Nobody I could see anyway.* I knew something was here. I could feel it.

Later that night, as I was falling asleep, I noticed one of the canned lights in the kitchen ceiling was flickering. A few seconds later it completely exploded, sending tiny shards of glass all over the room. I've never seen a light bulb shatter like this before. After that, if I kept the lights on all night, it never failed, one of the lights would explode. I had no choice but to keep the lights off. It never happened during the day either, only at night. I probably should have called an electrician, but it was a brand-new home and deep down I already knew they wouldn't find anything. I waited a week and tried to leave the lights in the kitchen on again. I really felt better having some light in the room with me. Sure enough, it happened again, and this time all five lights exploded at the same time. It was so loud it woke both Jeff and Stephanie up.

Jeff stayed up to help me find all the broken glass. The lights didn't just shatter, they blew like a bomb and sent glass flying everywhere. We were finding glass shards for days. I finally got Stephanie back to bed, and it was time for me to try to get some sleep. I dreaded night-time. I was becoming paranoid to fall asleep and afraid of what waited for me in the dark. Whatever is here likes to wait until I'm drifting off to sleep before it strikes. Tonight was no different. As I began falling asleep, I felt something gently touching my foot. At first, it felt like someone was caressing my foot with a feather. It started off very gentle, almost loving at first, until it reached my calf. Then it became much more aggressive. It started squeezing my leg, digging what felt like razor-sharp fingernails into my skin. I jumped off the couch, and it stopped. Sleep won't be coming for me tonight. I sat up all night waiting for the sun to rise. There's nothing to do in the middle of the night and television is brutal. Unless you love infomercials, there's nothing to watch.

Nights seemed so endless to me.

The following morning I passed Jeff in the hallway on my way to the bathroom.

"Morning babe,"

No answer.

"Jeff, morning."

Again, no answer.

I was getting angry and almost yelled at Jeff for being so rude when something caught my eye. Right as I was walking into the bathroom, I thought I caught a glimpse of Jeff inside the bedroom. He was standing next to the bed, stretching like he always does every morning when he first gets out of bed. I turned to look back down the hallway, but nothing was there. How the hell did I just pass Jeff in the hallway, but he's also in the bedroom, just barely out of bed?

What the hell was that thing I just saw in the hall?

I'm sleep deprived, but not enough to have hallucinations. I know I saw Jeff in the hallway and then again in the bedroom. The Jeff in the hallway wouldn't respond to me and now that I think about it, he didn't really look at me, either. I'm not sure if I even saw his face, but I still knew it was Jeff. I mean, I thought I knew it was Jeff, but obvi-ously it wasn't. The real question is, what did I just see in the hallway?

Sometimes things that happen here are too bizarre for me to explain. I have to give myself time to calm down before I can attempt to talk about it. Especially to Jeff. Perhaps it's because I'm still struggling to understand it myself. I'm also afraid to talk about the paranormal activity while I'm still inside the house because I'm feeling constantly watched. I'm afraid I will anger whatever is here and the activity will only get worse. I also couldn't wrap my brain around the significance of what had just taken place. Until I realized, *wait a minute,* there's no way that could have happened, and there's really no logical explanation for any of it. That's when it hits you. The truth is, you're dealing with something paranormal and out of the realm of human understanding.

At least it was beyond mine.

After seeing two Jeff's, things escalated. Everything was going nuts. Most of the time I thought I was losing my mind. Activity was out the window. Everything from visuals, to sounds, to smells, you name it. It wasn't a matter of if, it was a matter of when. Living here, in this dream house of horrors, was like moving into the worst nightmare I could have ever imagined. I had no peace. I was tired all the time. The house was sucking the life out of me and I was constantly sick. Jeff was changing. He was getting angrier. Stephanie was having trouble concentrating in school. I didn't know it, but I was getting depressed. I was even contemplating suicide.

It was at this point when I started hearing the voices.

I also stopped being able to warn myself inside my nightmares it's not real, it's just a bad dream and to wake up. Only now, I can't wake up. I'm screaming in my dream, but I can't wake myself up, and I'm losing the ability to recognize the difference between sleep and reality.

If that weren't bad enough . . .

I didn't know it yet, but I was being tormented by something that wasn't of this world, and it wasn't human.

I was standing at the entrance to the hallway when I saw a creature at the far end as tall as the ceiling. It was massive. To my surprise, the creature spoke. It called me "Goonie." My nickname as a child was Goonie. My brother couldn't pronounce my name, so instead of calling me Julie, he called me Goonie. It stuck and after a while, everyone called me Goonie.

Then it spoke again, "You are very special to me, and I am here for you."

I've never been more terrified in my entire life.

This thing was so huge. I was afraid it would consume me. It started walking toward me. I could feel an icy breeze engulfing my body and the sense of impending doom overwhelmed my mind. Without thinking, I yelled at it. I yelled out for God to help me and then I closed my eyes and recited these words over, and over again.

"I belong to the light, I belong to the light, I belong to the light."

Before I felt brave enough to open my eyes, I could already feel its evil presence had left. The room warmed, and I felt safe. At least for now.

Even though I sensed it was gone, it wasn't completely gone. Off in the distance, I still heard it. It made the most disgusting guttural growl I've ever heard. It really sounded pissed. I knew it was coming back to punish me for reaching out to God. I just knew it.

As soon as that thing stopped growling, the water in the kitchen turned on. Not really a hard-running stream, more like a gentle flow of water that turned on by itself. I walked into the kitchen and turned off the water. It surprised me how shaky my legs had become. As soon as I got back to the couch, the water had turned on again, but this time it was a hard-running stream of scorching hot water. When I went back into the kitchen to turn the water off, I'm shocked at the amount of steam flowing up from the sink. Then something remarkable happened. I watched in horror as the water moved sideways out of the faucet and onto the floor. At the same time, the gas stove turned on shooting flames high enough to land on the cabinets above.

I turned off the stove, turned off the water, slapped the fire off the cabinets with the kitchen towel, grabbed my purse and ran from my home. I drove to an empty parking lot at the end of our neighborhood and sat there until I felt calm enough to drive. After about a half hour I decided to go back to my religious book store for some advice. The priest from Saint Joe's was standing inside the Catholic bookstore when I walked in.

"Father, good afternoon, do you have a minute?"

"Sure, what can I help you with?"

"I desperately need your help. It's out of control and I fear something is trying to kill me."

"Julie, you know how I feel about this. Nothing is inside your home, and it's not trying to kill you. Did you take my advice and go see a psychiatrist?"

Can I punch a priest in the face and get away with it?

I didn't say or do anything. I'm humiliated and embarrassed. Not an unfamiliar feeling. This was a daily occurrence when I attended Catholic school. I waited for the jerk to leave and then I walked over to the counter to talk to the girl who worked there. She didn't even wait for me to talk before she said,

"Take this holy water. Bless every doorway, every window, the television, mirrors . . . everything. Say your prayers at the same time." As I made my way to the door, she added, "Screw that stupid priest."

I turned back around with a smile on my face for the first time in, I don't remember when. I thanked her and walked out.

I didn't waste any time. I went home and did exactly what she told me to do. I have used holy water many times before, but not as extensively as she recommended. Maybe I just hadn't done a good enough job. I tried to be vigilant and blessed the house with holy water and sage every day, but after a while it becomes a chore and it's easy to get complacent. Feeling safe was my biggest mistake. It's easy to lull yourself into a false sense of security. Especially when the activity has quieted down. Those are the moments you need vigilance the most. I learned everything the hard way, and this was no different.

The holy water worked really well, but only for a short time. When it wore off everything got worse. It started with tapping sounds, then it turned to scratching, then knocking. When I refused to acknowledge it, the knocks became aggressive. If it was a person knocking that hard, their knuckles would be sore. I didn't realize at the time, but I really should have been cleansing the house with sage at least once or twice every single day. Even at that, I'm not sure if it would have been enough. I fear this thing might be demonic. Perhaps it wouldn't have come back with as much vengeance each time if I'd been more careful.

Who knows, but as I look back, I realize it was just playing with me. It really hadn't gone full force on any of us yet. I believe this thing was so powerful it could have destroyed us all with the flick of a claw.

Yes, I said claw. I found out later . . . it had claws.

How did I find out? I found out when IT helped me wash my hair one day in the shower. I swear, it picked the most awkward times and the most vulnerable places to make itself known. I was in the middle of washing my hair when I felt an extra set of hands on my head. As soon as I felt the fingers, they turned to claws that were forcefully trying to dig into my scalp. I screamed and almost ran through the shower glass door. It was so painful; it felt like multiple knives were digging into my skull. I was so frantic I tripped and fell out of the shower. I had blood dripping from my head all over the new rug I just bought. Blood was everywhere. I didn't realize how bloody head wounds can be.

I stopped using the shower in the bedroom where I was whistled at by something I couldn't see. Now I'm being attacked in the only other shower we have. *The only shower I felt safe in.* This time it was an outright physical attack. I'm not safe anywhere and I'm especially vulnerable in the shower.

I'm never showering again.

17

To witness the supernatural with your own eyes can be life changing. Experiencing something first hand that science would most likely debunk as not being physically possible can make a person question everything they once believed. It can also make you feel as if you're losing your mind. Having a connection to the spirit world can be exhausting. It was pulling my energy, keeping me awake at night, and it even drained me to the point of making me physically ill. I don't think I can blame all my illnesses on the paranormal, but sometimes I wonder just how much of it was because of the spirit world.

I was getting depressed. I was contemplating suicide, but not seriously. It was more like the idea randomly popped into my head. Most of the time it didn't feel like the thought even came from me. It felt more like someone or something was downloading it into my brain. Before moving here, I never had to question if a thought was my own or not. If a thought popped into my head, I knew I was the only person who put it there. Now it's different. This time I knew without a doubt these weren't my own thoughts. I felt tormented. My emotions were a mixture of sadness, despair, anger and confusion.

When I was a kid, my mother often threatened to kill herself. *She never once attempted it.* I believe she was just trying to get attention. I know how it made me feel and I would never do that to Stephanie. My brother and I begged our father to get mom some help. We were just kids, what could we do? Our childhood was hell. They abused me in Catholic school and then I went home to a mentally ill, abusive mother. Somehow, I survived all that. Hopefully, I will survive this, too. I've really survived a lot. When I think about it, this doesn't differ that much from dealing with a scary mother or terrifying nuns. There is one major difference, however. When I was a child, I could see what form the monsters took when they were torturing me. Nowadays, they aren't always visible, and that puts it on a whole new level of fear.

Every time I got comfortable and let my guard down, that's when they would come back for more. Today was no different. I left Jeff at home with Stephanie so I could run to the store and get something for dinner. When I left, Stephanie was playing with a friend in her room and Jeff was watching television. About a half hour into my grocery shopping, Jeff called me.

"No babe, I'm still at the grocery store, why?"

"Oh nothing, I just thought you were home."

"Jeff, something happened to you, didn't it?"

"Never mind."

Click.

He's freaked out. He just doesn't know how to talk about it yet. I remember how I felt the first time. It took me a week before I could talk to anyone about it. I knew this day would be a turning point for us. Am I finally going to have someone I can talk to who will believe me? I better not get my hopes up, but I secretly hoped something happened to Jeff just so I don't have to feel so alone anymore.

After dinner, I sat down to talk to Jeff. It surprised me how willing he was to talk about it. He even seemed uncomfortable discussing it while we were inside the house. I asked him if he would like to go outside to talk, and he said he thought that would be best. Then he added, "You never know who's listening." Stephanie still had a friend over, so we felt comfortable going outside.

"So, tell me what happened? Something paranormal, obviously, or I'm assuming it is."

"Can I talk now?"

"Yeah, sorry, babe. I'm just a little excited you had an experience."

"Oh yeah, it's fucking awesome. Julie, it scared the shit out of me and I still can't wrap my head around it."

"Just take a deep breath, start at the beginning and tell me what happened."

Damn, this is so awesome . . .

"Ok, you had just left, and I thought you were coming back because you forgot something. I heard the back door in the utility room open, I heard footsteps coming up the hallway toward me, then I heard your voice calling out my name."

"And . . . "

"Then nothing, you never appeared. So, I waited another minute then called you and you were still at the grocery store."

"Wow babe, that's the same thing that happened to me. My first major paranormal event was the same thing you just experienced, only it was you calling out my name."

"Julie, it's time we get some help. Can you do some research tomorrow and call someone in here to help us? I don't mean to call another priest. Screw them, they never helped us anyway and when it helped it never lasted long. I believe we have something malevolent in our home and I feel horrible I can't fix it. I'm the man of the house, it's my job to fix everything, but I don't know how to tackle this."

"Babe, it's ok. Now that we understand what the other is going through, together we can conquer anything."

I tried to stay cool, but I was so glad Jeff was finally experiencing the same things as me, and now he realizes everything I'd told him was true. It was pure confirmation for me. I think when someone tells you such a fantastical story, you try to rationalize it. I'm sure he wanted to believe me, but, how could he? Until you experience it for yourself it's nearly impossible to relate. Plus, like most men, he's incredibly skeptical and everything I told him probably came across as far-fetched. I'm sure he questioned my sanity many times. I know I did and probably still do.

Jeff wasn't the type of person to just believe it. He had to see it with his own eyes, experience it for himself. It's not within him to believe anything like that, even with a minor experience. I think this time it was big enough to get Jeff's attention. He would always find some rational way to explain it away or debunk it. I had a moment of, "Oh thank God, I'm not crazy." That quickly turned to the feeling of, "oh shit, something really is happening in our brand-new dream house."

Some dream house. . .

At least I know who I'm not calling for help. The last priest we went to refused to help me. He wouldn't step foot inside our home. *Big chicken.* How do I give this to another innocent person to fight? This was more than just cleansing a home to me. This was a fight between good and evil to get my home back.

Perhaps even a fight for my soul.

I still feel afraid, but now I'm feeling a sense of renewal. I feel a new power of hope coming from deep within me. There is strength in numbers and knowing I finally have Jeff on my side is comforting. I'm feeling abandoned by the priest and the church, but why would I continue to hope for anything from this church? The same place that tied me to my chair in first grade. *What was I thinking?*

I was desperate for help and looked to them for divine intervention. For the priest to turn his back on me? That in itself is diabolical. It's the final straw. I will never step foot back inside that church. It feels awkward to me even calling it a church. A church should be a place of refuge, a place of peace and light; a sanctuary. It's never represented that for me, so it's time to move on. I will reach out to someone in the paranormal field, but if they can't help us, then what? All I can do is try. I will also try to be stronger, have no fear and call upon my higher power for help.

What else could I do?

It was all on me now. No help was coming, not from the Catholic church, anyway. At least they didn't kill my faith. I'm surprised, yet I also feel fortunate the hell I went through as a kid didn't destroy my faith. It only strengthened it. Sometimes I feel like I'm all alone in the wilderness, fighting the good fight and believing that someday, I just might prevail. I've got God on my side.

I hope.

It wasn't long before I found a paranormal group that was willing to come investigate our home. I'm feeling a sense of renewed hope that we are finally going to get some answers. Life was looking a little brighter and I'm excited to have some real professionals in the paranormal field looking into my little house of horrors. It feels a little like a natural high, a feeling I could definitely benefit from. Everything has been so gloomy and depressing lately. I've been so alone with this for far too long. The paranormal group was willing to move some appointments around to make time to come the very next week. The guy I talked to told me he considered ours an emergency.

"I haven't heard something as intense as your story in a very long time. I suspect you have some demonic activity, but I also suspect you could have something additional to demonic activity. Something along the lines of poltergeist activity."

"What's a poltergeist?"

"A poltergeist is a type of ghost or spirit responsible for physical attacks, loud noises and objects being moved around. They are noisy spirits that harass and torment their victims. Many people believe poltergeists are created by a living person who's experienced some form of abuse."

Well, that explains a lot.

"I have a question before I let you go. Once you find out what's here, will you be able to help us get rid of it?"

"Yes, of course. We have lots of people we can reach out to, like Reiki masters or mediums that can aid us in cleansing you and your home."

"Did you say cleanse me? Why would I need cleansing?"

"Let's just take it one step at a time. Can we come over around 11:00 p.m. next Tuesday?"

"Sure, but why so late?"

"We like to do our investigations at night because activity tends to be higher at night."

Not in my house.

"You are welcome to come anytime you like. I'm just grateful I finally found someone who can help me."

"Do you plan to be in the house when we investigate?"

"I never gave it any thought, but yes, we really don't have anywhere else to go. Can we stay during the investigation?"

"Yes, but we might be there all night long and most of our clients prefer to spend the night elsewhere."

"Oh ok, well I will talk it over with my husband. As long as we are quiet and stay out of your way, I'd kind of like to see how you do your investigations. Just in case I ever need to do one of my own, I'd like to follow you around and learn from you, if that's alright."

"Sure, no problem."

There's no way in hell I am giving total strangers access to my house without me being there. This is making me feel a little weird, but I'm desperate for help. Maybe I'm just feeling anxious. I really need to trust someone.

Because I'm so nervous talking about the activity in our home while still inside our house . . . speaking to the paranormal investigator over the phone was no different. I was feeling increasingly uncomfortable with the fact that I had just openly talked about it. I'm fearful I gave a "head's up" to whatever was here. I'm also afraid of retaliation for what I was attempting to do . . . rid my house of it once and for all.

I never dreamed for a second it wouldn't be me it retaliated against. This is exactly how the mafia took out revenge on a traitor or a snitch. Maybe whatever was here terrorizing me used to be involved with the mafia, or maybe my father had some business dealings with them and pissed them off, so now they're here tormenting me from the afterlife. Whatever it is, *I will never know for sure,* but I have always suspected my father had ties to the mafia. When the mafia wanted to punish someone, they didn't kill them, instead they went after their family members. Sometimes the mafia even made them watch while they inflicted pain on their loved ones. It's effective torture, that's for sure. Luckily for me, I never had to experience that level of violence.

This time Jeff was the target. It wanted Jeff to feel its power. It had plans for me, too, but that wasn't coming until later. I'm very grateful Jeff didn't die because he easily could have. Jeff and I had a normal, uneventful evening. In fact, everything seemed to be almost too quiet. We went to bed around 11:30 p.m. I was still sleeping on the couch, holding onto my grandma's rosary. Jeff went into the bedroom and closed the door. Around 3:00 a.m. I thought I heard his door open. It wasn't anything too alarming, Jeff usually got up during the night to use the bathroom. However, I never heard him go into the bathroom or close the bedroom door again. I was glad Jeff woke me up. I was in the middle of a terrible nightmare and I was glad to be out of it.

I waited a few minutes, got fully awake, then went to check on Jeff. I'm sure everything is fine, but I can't get back to sleep until I know for sure. I threw off my blanket, got up and almost felt dizzy as I walked up the hallway. Maybe it's the blood pressure medication, I told myself. I try not to blame everything on the paranormal.

I got halfway up the hallway when I heard Jeff's car engine turn over. Someone was in the garage starting Jeff's car? Perhaps someone found a way inside our garage and they are stealing his truck. I went to get Jeff out of bed to investigate with me, but he wasn't there. I went to take a peek in the garage. Maybe Jeff was called out on a job or something, not that uncommon in the janitorial business. He used to get called out frequently at night, although that hasn't happened much lately. Right as I was about to open the door that led to the garage, Jeff came flying through it. He was shaking and pale.

"Jeff, what's going on?"

"I don't know. I just woke up. I don't understand how I ended up in the garage."

I went into the garage to check on the car and the stench almost knocked me out. The smell of exhaust and rotten eggs was thick inside the garage.

"Jeff, did you leave the garage door down when you started your truck?"

"I don't know, I guess. I don't really know what's going on, Julie, I think I was sleepwalking or something."

It absolutely terrified me because deep down I already knew something evil was here and it just tried to kill my husband. I don't believe for a second, he was "just" sleep walking. I'm convinced something led him to the garage and influenced him to start his truck with the garage door down. It was trying to kill Jeff. I have no doubt about it. The weirdest part was the fact that I woke up from a nightmare where I was dreaming Jeff was killing himself inside his truck in exactly the same manner. Although I don't understand how it happened, I also know this . . .

That was no coincidence.

I blamed myself. This is my punishment for calling out for help. I just pray we can hold on until next week. Maybe I should call them and see if they can come any sooner. I'm on a whole new level of scared now. What is going to happen to us before they can even get here?

I called the paranormal investigator, but they were in the middle of another important case and couldn't get away. It's ok, we only have five more days to get through. I will just do as much as I can to protect ourselves. I will sage at least twice a day, spray some more holy water on everything and recite the "Saint Michael" prayer until help can arrive. It can't get here soon enough.

I hoped that was the end of the attack on Jeff, but it wasn't. It attacked again the very next night. This time it was Jeff who experienced a nightmare. He claimed it was just a nightmare, but I believe it was real. He said he dreamed that a woman who looked exactly like me came to him in a dream.

"Even though it was just a dream, it was incredibly vivid, and it felt very real to me. The woman looked and sounded exactly like you, but I knew it wasn't you."

He sensed she was trying to trick him.

He asked her to leave. Instead, she began touching him sensually. When she leaned in to kiss him, that's when things took a turn for the worse. She turned into what he referred to as very, "old hag looking" and then he really freaked out because she decomposed. She started attacking him . . . biting and scratching, then she sat on his chest with such force it made it nearly impossible for Jeff to breathe. This rendered him paralyzed. In his desperation to get away from her, he woke himself up.

He was so freaked out by the dream he came and woke me up to talk about it instead of waiting until morning. Even though he desperately needed to talk about it, Jeff really struggled to understand it. I knew it wasn't a dream at all. This really happened, but it wanted Jeff to think it was just a nightmare. I did some research and I believe what visited Jeff was either an entity called, "The Old Hag" or it was a "Succubus." Either way, it's not good. Jeff also remembers smelling something similar to what a decomposing body mixed with urine would smell like. I know this dream or whatever it was will haunt Jeff for a very long time. Every one of my vivid nightmares has haunted me. Especially when they are recurring nightmares. Those really take a toll on me.

The next night the terror would come back around to me, but on a whole new level than I'd ever experienced. I'm positive I awakened something by contacting the paranormal investigators, and I really pissed it off. I wish I had left the house before calling anyone for help. At that point in time, I didn't think it could follow me outside of our home. *Boy, was I wrong.*

Jeff and I were growing more and more desperate for a way to stay awake. We were scared to death to fall asleep at night. However, no matter how much coffee we drank or how hard we tried, sleep eventually came.

I was being tormented by a demon in the form of a mimic, I just didn't know it yet. I started waking up between 3:00 and 3:33 in the morning. I used to find it so odd waking up right at 3:33, but I believe now there was some significance to it.

I started waking up with ghostly faces staring at me within inches of my own. Then the ghosts I couldn't recognize morphed into old friends of mine who had died. I've known many people who've died, and many of my friends died tragic deaths. Six friends from grade school committed suicide, three died in a bar shooting, and my best friend Debby died from ovarian cancer.

I could hear them calling out to me in my dreams, but then again, I wasn't so sure I was still asleep. The sounds were coming from inside the coat closet, the same closet I saw that little girl running in and out of. I've also heard them calling out to me from inside the walls in the hallway. Most of the time, though, the calls came from inside the coat closet. I'd wake up with my hand on the handle of the closet door, getting ready to open it. I have never sleep walked a day in my life, but here I am, waking up in front of the coat closet with my hand on the door.

The next night I had the same dream, only this time it led me to the large oval mirror that hung above the fireplace. I looked inside the mirror and I could see someone walking toward me. It was my old friend "Puff" from high school. Only one problem, he died years ago in a car accident. I heard him say, "Julie, I'm right here. I miss you. I'm coming to get you. We want you to join us." Puff reached his arm through the mirror to take my hand. As I reached up to take it, I woke with a jolt. I felt like I'd been electrocuted and my heart was pounding out of my chest. I was standing in front of the mirror drenched in sweat, but freezing cold at the same time. I'm feeling an overwhelming sense of dread and sorrow. I was shaking so hard I could barely move. When I got back to the couch, I discovered my Grandma Eva's rosary broke, and the beads were strewn all over the room. I sat down on the couch and cried. I felt so broken and alone. I seriously need help, now! The paranormal investigators can't come though. I wanted to call them again and beg for them to come sooner, but I'm sure there are others who have it worse than I do. I need to be patient. I made myself a pot of coffee and waited for morning to come.

Each night that followed, the activity in my dreams escalated. The next night, the visions started becoming more violent. I believe it was trying to talk me into killing myself.

"Your family doesn't care about you, why don't you kill yourself?"

At first, I thought my dreams were just visions or night terrors. Now I believe it was visits from demons who could shape shift into different forms. The dreams were so vivid and real I believe most of the time I was physically seeing them, but tricked into believing it was just a dream. They wanted to frighten me so they could feed off my fear, which was pure energy for them. Their end game was possession and control. I didn't need any paranormal investigators to explain this to me, I intuitively already knew it.

When trying to get me to take my own life wasn't working, they changed the message.

"Your family doesn't care about you, why don't you kill them?"

They wanted me to hurt my family. *This was real.* It was more than real; it was powerful. It either came to me as one, or many. At one time I heard it say the word "legion" which translates to mean "many." I knew this was bigger than anything I'd previously imagined, and I was in for the fight of my life. A fight for my family's life and the sanctity of our souls. I couldn't let this thing break me. I have to fight back. My family is in jeopardy and they desperately need me to save us all. I never wanted to hurt my family. I love them. It was inconceivable to even think about. I started trying to ignore it. That was a terrible mistake because how can you possibly control what's happening in your sleep?

The only thing that saved me and kept us alive while we waited for help to come was the power of prayer. That's it. I had exhausted all my options. Luckily for me, prayer never turned its back on me and neither did the angels I called on for help.

I've been putting all my eggs in the paranormal investigators' basket when I just needed to pray. Even though deep down I knew this already, I was so desperate for a knight in shining armor to ride in on a white horse and save us.

Too bad knights don't exist and we didn't have a horse.

18

The day I scheduled the paranormal investigators to arrive finally came. For me, not a day too soon. I was worrying we wouldn't make it. Thanks to my faith and prayer, we are still in one piece, feeling stronger than ever and ready to fight whatever we need to.

They arrived at exactly eleven p.m. just as they said they would. There were three investigators. Two guys and one girl. The guys' names were Matt and Brian, the girl's name was Stacy. Stacy was an intuitive who considered herself a medium with the ability to communicate with spirits. She was very helpful to me. She explained how ghosts came to be.

"Usually, to be a ghost, a person has to have died suddenly or cannot accept that death has occurred, or doesn't even know they are no longer in a physical body."

Then she added, "Only malevolent energies can inflict physical pain."

That made a chill go straight up my back.

"Stacy, from what we've experienced, I believe we have multiple malevolent entities here, so do whatever you need to do to protect yourselves."

Stacy noticed all the Catholic medals and holy crosses I had placed around our home.

"So, are you Catholic?"

"I consider myself a recovering Catholic."

"I see. Sounds like there's a lot of pain behind that statement."

"Well yes Stacy, you are intuitive!"

They were kind enough to let me watch them set up all the cameras and electronic gadgets they brought. I was definitely intrigued and had lots of questions, but I didn't want to slow them down or become too big of a pain. However, there was just one question I couldn't stop myself from asking.

"Have any of you had any experiences before with a demonic entity?"

Matt was the first to speak.

"I got attacked by one at Jory Park about a week ago. It left three scratches down the middle of my back that stung like hell."

"Pun intended?"

"Yep."

"Why does it hurt so much? I felt claws digging into my scalp. It was in the form of three deep cuts beginning at the top of my head and went all the way down to my neck. It bled like a mother, too."

"There's a significance to the number three. It's intended to mock the trinity. The Father, the Son, and the Holy Ghost. It burns to signify the fires in hell. Plus, your pain brings much pleasure to demons. They feed off of your energy. Doesn't matter whether it's the energy of fear or the energy of pain. They don't care, energy is energy and the more the better for them."

"Jesus!"

Mike continued.

"The best thing you can do is not be afraid and not . . ."

"Oh, sure thing, Mike. That's easier said than done."

"Yes, but if you want to conquer demons, you don't have a choice. You cannot ever show fear. Be strong and release all fear."

Stacy rolled her eyes.

"Ok Mike, can we please stop scaring our new client and get back to work?"

It was fun to watch how these guys ribbed each other. I'm not sure how good they were at their job, but they were definitely entertaining.

~

They were ready to begin their investigation, so I left them alone and joined Jeff in the front room. The group took some EVPs in the living room, then moved on to the garage. I remember saying a prayer for their safety when they went into the garage. Stacy was feeling some dread, and the last thing I wanted was for any of them to get hurt in my home.

They weren't in the garage for long. Stacy was the first to come running back inside the house, with the guys following closely behind her.

"You're not going to believe what just happened in the garage."

"Yeah, I'm sure I will. The weirdest things happen in there."

"Well, give me a second to catch my breath and wrap my head around what just happened to me."

"Can I get you something to drink?"

"I'd love a glass of water, thank you."

I went to get Stacy some cold water from the fridge while trying to stay light hearted with our conversation. I was dying to hear what had just taken place in the garage, but I didn't want her to feel rushed.

"I get it, take all the time you need to, Stacy. It usually hits me like that too, and I can't talk about it either right after it happens. Plus, do you think it's safe to talk about it while we are still inside the house?"

"Oh yeah, if they wanted to hear you it doesn't really matter where you are."

That answers a lot of questions.

"Most of the time I'm afraid to talk about what goes on here, while still here. Does that make sense?"

"Yes, but I'm positive whatever has attached to you inside this home is also following you whenever you leave."

Please don't say that, don't even think it.

"Julie, we just had the most remarkable experience in the garage."

Stacy sure recovered fast. I'm surprised she didn't need more time, but maybe she's more used to all of this than I am.

"A penny fell from the ceiling and landed on my shoulder. I turned on the light and we looked at the penny in complete amazement."

Then Matt spoke up.

"The weirdest part wasn't that the penny fell from above, what surprised me was the fact that the penny came from inside my pocket."

"You mean, something took the penny out of your pocket then dropped it from the ceiling and it hit Stacy on the shoulder?"

"Yep, that's exactly what happened. I even remember the date that was on the penny. It's an older date, so I checked it out to see if it was worth anything."

This sounds a little fishy . . .

I mean, who remembers the date of a penny that's inside their pocket? Maybe he does, but I'm feeling my "Spidey-sense" peak a little. That intuition or sixth sense that tells you something is bullshit. First, they didn't even want us here during their investigation. Maybe that's normal, it's not every day I invite paranormal investigators into my home. This is a first for me. Maybe I'm wrong to suspect them. I'm so used to being alone, I should be grateful for their help.

They never went back inside the garage. I guess their investigation was done, although they weren't in there very long. Who knows, maybe something scared them so badly they didn't want to go back. Their investigation continued in the hallway. They set up a camera to shoot the entire area, hoping to capture something. They also tried to record some EVPs. EVP stands for, "Electronic voice phenomena." In the spirit world, it's very hard to hear what the spirts are trying to communicate. So, if we can't hear with the naked ear what spirits are saying, hopefully a voice recorder will be able to pick it up. I don't know exactly how it works, but I find it fascinating. They also set up a grid of lights to flicker if anything walked through it.

I stayed out of their hair for the rest of the investigation. After about an hour, they started packing up their equipment.

"So, did you get anything you can share with us?"

Mike was the leader of the team, so he was the one I asked.

"We got a tremendous amount of EVPs and I think we even captured something on the camera in the hall. What we will need to do now is go home and begin the long journey of reviewing our equipment."

"Will you come back to share with us what you found out?"

"Yes, it will most likely be a few weeks before we can share with you what we captured."

"I can't wait."

Mike had a funny look on his face, so I asked him if anything was bothering him.

"Well, I don't want to say too much until we review what we captured. However, we caught some interesting chanting sounds, and we heard something through the EVP equipment and our spirit box that we all agree sounded demonic. I think you have multiple things going on here and frankly, I can't imagine having to live in this much activity."

"Mike, are we safe to stay here? Could it come down to the fact that we will just have to leave this house?"

Mike was silent for a moment before he spoke again and I could see he was in deep thought. I could also tell something really got to him.

"If it were my home, I'd list it tomorrow."

"Well, we can't do that. We spent all our money on the down payment. Plus, how can I, in good conscience, sell this place to some unsuspecting person? I really can't do it. I need to figure out what's here and get rid of it before I feel comfortable selling it."

Is demonic or spirit activity something you'd have to legally disclose when selling your home?

I just know I would never forgive myself if I dumped this problem on someone else. I'd rather burn the house to the ground then let another family go through what we have. Now I'm feeling overwhelming regret just talking about this inside the house. I know something is always listening and watching, and it especially watches me. I've always been the prime target, which is another reason I don't feel moving would make that big of a difference. What if whatever is here just follows us to another home?

19

I waited over two months to hear from the paranormal group. I finally started calling them, but nobody returned my calls. Aside from not calling me back, they never returned to share what they captured. I called Mike multiple times, left a ton of phone messages, but he never called me back. I finally just gave up.

Looks like my Spidey-sense turned out to be right about this group. What a bunch of frauds. I was incredibly upset. Now I'm left wondering, what was their agenda? We think they were just here pretending to be paranormal investigators. Jeff thought they were casing our home so they could rip us off at a later time. Total frauds and a total waste of time. The fact that they are completely blowing me off is only adding to my anger. I'm afraid they just might come back when we're gone and clean us out. Oh great, just what I need, one more thing to worry about.

I'm back at square one again. I've not only been disappointed by a couple of priests, I can now add the paranormal investigators to the list. How do you do that to desperate people? I also wondered; could they have found something so horrific here that they were too afraid to come back? No excuse, they owed me at least a phone call. It really makes them look like frauds. After a year of leaving messages, trying to get them to talk to me, I finally gave up for good. I guess I may never know what really happened to them.

At least the activity didn't ramp up too much after the investigation, probably because it really wasn't much of one. Not at all threatening, so the entities here probably got a good laugh instead. Will I ever find anyone to help me? I have little hope for that at this point. For now, it's all up to me. All I can do is deal with the day-to-day activity. At least I learned a few techniques along the way. I will continue to sage regularly, spread blessed salt across all thresholds including window sills, and spray down the house with holy water. I even memorized my favorite Saint Michael prayer. Even though the priest at St. Joe's wouldn't come to our home to bless it, he didn't stop me from making frequent trips to fill up my containers of blessed salt and holy water. At least he did that much for me.

A few weeks went by with nothing more than the normal knocks, footsteps and scary dreams. All of which I've become accustomed to. This morning was different. In my wildest imagination, I couldn't have dreamed of something like this. It's so foreign to my ability to comprehend, and I'm still incredibly mystified by it all.

I was in the bathroom off the master bedroom getting ready for work. I had just gotten out of the shower. Luckily with no whistles, scratches or anything scaring me. I really hate taking a shower these days, especially when I'm all alone in the house. Since I was physically attacked in the bathroom down the hall, I'm back to showering in the master bedroom again. The shower and toilet are at the far end of the master bathroom behind a door. The bathroom is quite large with a huge jetted tub next to a counter and a sink. On the other side of the room is an even larger counter with a sink. Above the sinks are large rectangular mirrors. Both mirrors are directly across the room from one another.

I was looking in the mirror in front of me while brushing my hair. Because the mirrors are opposite one another, I can see my reflection in the mirror directly behind me. This wouldn't be weird if I were looking at the back side of my head. What was unusual today was the fact that I was seeing myself in the mirror behind me, looking directly at me. If it really was my reflection, I would be looking at the back side of my body, not my face. I quickly turned around, and my image was still there, looking straight back at me. At the same time, I saw a sinister-looking grin come over my face in the reflection, but I'm not smiling. I freaked and ran out of the bathroom. Halfway to the kitchen, I heard laughter directly behind me. The sinister laughter followed me all the way into the kitchen, growing louder and louder with each passing second.

This time, instead of running out of the house like I normally do, I began to pray. As soon as I finished my prayer, I heard a deep guttural voice say, "Your God can't save you now." I know I shouldn't have provoked it, but I was at the end of my rope. I mean, how much can a girl take?

I yelled back at it, "Leave me alone unclean spirit and get the hell out of my house." That's when I felt the intense burning sensation on the front of my left leg. It burned and stung worse than the last time. I tried to look down at my leg, but I couldn't move. It was holding me in some kind of telepathic trap. I was frozen as it took over my mind and my body.

I've never been this terrified before.

It's coming closer to me, but there's nothing I can do. I'm completely paralyzed. I can feel it breathing down the back of my neck. I'm getting goosebumps all over my body. I feel ice-cold finger-nails pierce my neck and slowly travel down the middle of my back as if it were tracing my spine; its icy fingers slowing digging deep into my flesh. I'm in a tremendous amount of pain. I struggled so hard to breathe it made me choke. Impending doom is flooding over me. Mentally, I try telling myself to slow down my breathing and try to relax.

Who am I kidding?

I'm in the grip of a demonic entity that's holding me prisoner. It's in complete control of my body, and my mind was in a state of panic. Calming down was not an option. Then I heard it growl. This thing was so close to my left ear and the stench was overwhelming. This sounds exactly like the growl I heard in the master bedroom when I was closing the blinds, but this time is different. This time I'm going to die. This thing is finally going to kill me. I feel three more deep scratches down my left side. I want to cry out in agony, but I can't.

The human spirit is pretty amazing. Even though I was in a state of pure panic, I fought back. My fight or flight response was at full force. I've been able to actually lift my car out of a ditch during moments of extreme stress. I believe our minds can give our bodies super human strength when fear and adrenaline combine. Problem was, even with my own added strength, this thing was much stronger than me. Not to mention, I'm still frozen. No matter how hard I tried, I wasn't going anywhere.

How can something invisible have so much strength? My mind was still working, it can't possibly freeze my thoughts, too. *I hope.* I can't move, but I'm fairly certain I can still use my mind. I called out to Saint Michael inside my head.

"Come save me, Saint Michael, and bring all your warrior angels with you."

Almost immediately, I broke free. Off in the distance I heard the sound of wings making flapping noises, all in unison. I never saw the wings, but I could hear them. It sounded the same as when geese exited the lake at the same time. There's a definite sound to it. I instinctively knew I was in the presence of light and love. I've never felt more protected in my entire life. I had the same feeling when I had my near-death experience back when I was fifteen. Then a thought came to my mind. *If only I could feel this way all the time.* I believe when I die, I will feel euphoric all the time and the demon knew it. I believe they can read our minds, know our desires, our weaknesses, and most of all, they know what we fear.

I heard the demon speak . . .

"You can feel this way all the time. All you have to do is kill yourself. Just die, it's easy. All your problems will go away and you will live like you've never lived before."

So many sweet promises from an evil serpent.

I've had enough. I'm on a mission to rid myself and our home of this evil. I'm not exactly sure how yet, but I know I'm stronger than this thing. I have God with his warrior angels on my side. Evil doesn't stand a chance.

For reasons still unbeknownst to me, I gained more power and strength than ever before. I felt like I was finally ready to fight this thing. I believe Saint Michael gave me that strength. How could it have come from inside of me? Maybe I'm underestimating myself. Being surrounded by angels is truly an amazing experience. I never felt more at peace.

I yelled to the unclean spirit, "I demand, in the name of God, tell me your name."

I'm not even sure why I did that, but years later I would learn that it's dangerous to use a demons name. *I actually got a name.* The name I heard was, "Magnus." As soon as I heard the name, the entity was gone. Still, I felt a sense of victory. This was the first time I was scared out of my wits and didn't run out of my house. Even though I was in a lot of pain and shaken, I felt victorious. I felt like this was the beginning of my journey to becoming a spiritual warrior. I'm ready to take my house back. Still, I have to be careful and not get too cocky for fear it could retaliate. I'm still not sure what I'm dealing with. Demons are notorious liars. I wasn't just in a fight for my life, I was in a fight for my soul.

I just didn't know it yet.

I did some more research on our property. I discovered that a person by the name of Manfred died in a horrific rock crushing accident at the rock quarry which is now our lake. He was working with a rock crusher when the equipment jammed. He tried to free the jam, but his harness became tangled in the conveyor belt. He was dragged into the rock crusher and mashed to death. What a horrible and tragic way to die. Could he be who's haunting my house and not a demon? Why is he picking on me? He's acting like a demonic entity and scaring the shit out of me. Maybe his anger about his untimely death is causing him to be stuck here instead of crossing over. Maybe he doesn't even know he's dead. All these thoughts are flooding my mind. Perhaps I'm thinking too much. I'm just desperate to find a way to ease my mind. It's much less terrifying if it's just a person here and not some monster I really don't want to believe exists.

I need more information and I think I know where to get it. A friend of mine recently told me about a new store that just opened up in our area. It's a metaphysical store. They also have counselors there who can help. I figured, why not? Everything else I've tried has failed. Maybe some spiritual guidance outside of the church is exactly what I need. To me, it felt like my last resort.

Right now, though, it's time for bed, and that brings up a whole new set of issues. I desperately need to sleep, but I'm afraid to. Some nights I can't tell if my dreams are real or not. They are so frightening and vivid lately. I dread the nighttime. I'm terrified to go to sleep.

20

I woke to the sound of heavy knocking at the front door. There was something incredibly intense and frantic behind those knocks. It wasn't the tap, tap, tap sound like girl scouts selling cookies, it was more like bam, bam, bam . . . I'm breaking down this door.

I jumped off the couch and looked at the time. It was exactly 3:33 in the morning. Who could be knocking on our door at this hour? I didn't know who *or what* was at our front door, but I instinctively knew better than to open it. There's no way I'm opening that door. At the same moment I started hearing what sounded like a man on the other side frantically yelling, "Open the door, open the door, open the door. This is an emergency, emergency, emergency. Let us in, let us in, let us in."

I grabbed my phone and dialed 911 instead of opening the front door. It's so against my nature not to answer the door, especially when someone's outside screaming for help. I felt like something was warning me not to. I sensed whatever was at my door wasn't human and if I opened the door, we'd all be dead. I hadn't put it together yet, but everything he said, was said in sets of three. What I've learned is, when something paranormal happens in sets of three it typically relates to an evil force. It's their way of mocking the holy trinity . . . Father, Son, and Holy Ghost.

He also said, "Let *us* in," so there must have been more than just one on the other side of the door. This was a demon. I didn't know it at the time, but I'm glad I listened to my intuition. I don't believe I would be around to tell this story if I had opened the door and invited evil into our home.

Jeff sprang out of bed and ran down the hallway. It was all I could do to keep him from opening the front door. I've never seen him look more terrified. "Jeff, I beg you, do not open that door." Jeff ignored me and reached for the door. The moment his hand touched the door handle, the knocking and yelling grew stronger, louder and definitely angrier. Jeff jerked his hand back and hollered out in pain. "The door handle just burned my hand. How the hell did that happen?" He turned his hand over and it was already beginning to welt.

The police finally arrived. Only ten minutes had passed since I called 911, but it felt like so much longer. Now that I'm positive it's not a human on the other side of our door . . . I'm afraid for the officers' safety. I said a prayer for all of us. The minute the police got to our front door, the knocking stopped. The officers did a thorough search of our property and found nothing.

This was no way a human or a spirit. This had to be demonic. The knocking was too intense, and the voice was strong and guttural. I believe whatever was out there came close to knocking our front door down, I couldn't believe the force behind those knocks. This is a big heavy door, too. When the police drove away, I heard that sinister laughter again. Jeff heard it too. Jeff yelled and provoked it. I begged him to stop. This time it was Jeff's turn to get scratched.

"Jeff, I warned you not to provoke it."

"Screw that, Julie, this is my home and I'll be damned if something I can't even see is going to threaten us."

That's what I'm afraid of. I'm terrified we're already damned, or cursed, or Lord knows what.

I cleaned Jeff's wounds, then we tried to get a little rest before the sun came up. Jeff was on his way back to bed when he noticed something strange on the wainscoting in the hallway.

"Julie, come take a look at this."

By this time, nothing was going to shock me.

Or so I thought.

As I walked down the hall toward Jeff, the smell of sulfur attacked my senses. Then it switched to something worse, the smell of decaying flesh.

"Jeff, what the heck, I can't take this."

"What are you talking about?"

"Can't you smell it? It smells like rotten eggs and rotting flesh all mixed into one."

"No, I don't smell anything, but I need you to look at what's on the wall."

I looked over and saw this oozing, thick, clear gelatinous liquid running down the wall. I couldn't tell where it was coming from and when I tried to clean it, more appeared in its place. It reminded me of when I tried to clean the red marking off the fireplace mantle.

"Jeff, I'm exhausted. Can I deal with this tomorrow? I desperately need some sleep and I'm sure you do, too."

Jeff reached over and gave me the biggest, most loving hug he's given me in a really long time. We've been so busy with all the craziness surrounding us, we forgot about us. Our relationship has taken a back burner to all this. He gave me a kiss, and I thought he was going to tell me goodnight when he surprised me by saying,

"Yeah, then we need to find a bulldozer in the morning and flatten this nightmare of a house."

Finally!

I couldn't help but laugh when he said that. To think . . . all this time I felt so completely alone when we were both feeling the same thing.

"Well babe, good idea until the insurance company finds out we were the ones who dozed it. Then what will we do? I guess we could go camp out at my parents."

"No way, I'd rather live in this haunted nightmare."

"Me too!"

At least this time I'm going to bed with a much lighter feeling in my heart. I'm so tired nothing is going to get to me tonight. I'm going to sleep like a dead person.

I couldn't have been more wrong. I don't remember falling asleep, nor do I know how long I'd been asleep. I woke up because a hand was on my shoulder, nudging me to wake up. My first thought was that it was Jeff, but this wasn't Jeff. It was a little boy around the age of eight with large hollow dark eyes. He was wearing a red plaid shirt tucked into dirty blue jeans held up by suspenders. He reminded me of Huckleberry Finn. Suddenly it hit me, his shirt was the same pattern as the dress worn by the little girl spirit I keep seeing.

He stared at me for an uncomfortable amount of time, then his face morphed into this larger than normal creepy grin. I could see his teeth when he smiled. They were long and pointed at the ends and looked just like knives. I sat there watching as he walked away from me and disappeared inside the hall closet. I remembered thinking I should run and get away from him, but I couldn't move. I wasn't even sure I was awake. I sat there in amazement as he walked back out of the coat closet holding hands with the little girl. Now I see her for what she truly is.

A demon.

The crucifix I hung above the front door violently flew off the wall and landed at my feet. The demon children walked in strange jerky motions. They reminded me of marionette's. Next came the ungodly stench circulating throughout the room. The smell rotated between sulfur and rotting flesh. This is when things got really bad. The little girl moved back into the coat closet, then reappeared looking completely different. She wasn't that innocent little girl spirit anymore. She spoke in a deep, gravelly voice. She morphed into this thing with long razor-sharp teeth and hollow black eyes resembling that of the little boy. They were dressed like they could have been twins in a very sick and twisted way.

Her head changed as well. The beautiful long curly hair with the red plaid bow quickly turned into the most gaud awful medusa looking mop of hair I'd ever seen. I started feeling sick to my stomach. She walked over to the hallway where the wainscoting had previously dripped the thick clear gelatinous fluid. When she got to the wall, her feet turned into hooves. She touched the wall and turned the clear fluid into blood. I broke out in a cold sweat. This thing kept speaking, but I couldn't quite make out what it was saying. They were speaking in a dialect I've never heard before.

I was so freaked out I started screaming, which surprised even me. I'm not the type of girl to scream. It just came out of me in a primal sort of way. I needed help, and I desperately needed to get away from these scary creatures. Then a word popped into my head from out of nowhere. The word was "pray." I began praying the "Our Father" prayer.

Our Father, who art in Heaven, hallowed be thy name. Thy kingdom come thy will be done . . .

"Julie, wake up!"

I woke up to Jeff shaking my shoulders and yelling in my face to wake up.

"Jeff, did you see those creatures?"

"Julie, you're just having a bad dream."

"No, I'm not, Jeff, they were real."

I had to prove to Jeff I wasn't dreaming. I got up and ran toward the hallway. When I got to the wainscoting against the wall, I couldn't believe what I saw. To my amazement, the wall was dripping in blood.

"Jeff, come down here and look at this. You will understand when you see it."

Jeff saw the red blood dripping down the wall. He just stood there staring at the bloody wall for the longest time. It was like he couldn't speak. I think he was in shock.

"Jeff, are you alright?"

This was hitting Jeff pretty hard. I guess even tough guys sometimes struggle to wrap their head's around this kind of thing.

The color had completely drained from Jeff's face. I've never seen him this scared before. Jeff is a macho, tough guy. Nothing shakes him. We both just stood there. Neither one of us knew what to do.

We were struggling to understand something that was so far

beyond our ability to comprehend. The only thing I knew for sure at this point was that I needed some serious help.

I've experienced a ton more than Jeff, but I still struggled with it. I know one thing for sure.

My nightmares really had morphed into reality.

21

Neither one of us was getting anymore sleep. We barely even talked about it. What could we say? Besides, I don't feel comfortable talking about the activity while still inside our home. I'm convinced we are constantly being watched these days, which completely creeps me out. We just sat quietly together watching silly infomercials on TV until the sun came up.

There was so much I wanted to say, but couldn't. My own thoughts were racing inside my head. I wanted to tell Jeff about my nightmares. Especially the one with the lizard. I really wanted to convince myself that it was just a bad dream. *A really bad dream.* Now, I'm certain that thing was real. I've had so many recurring nightmares lately. Were they really just dreams? Or, is something from another dimension visiting me while I'm vulnerable in my dream state? Could I be manifesting what I fear? This is just too much. First the knocks at the front door and now this? I don't know how much more I can take.

Watching the sunrise was a welcoming sight for the both of us. I think we just needed some normalcy. Jeff got up to take a shower. Soon he will leave me alone again to run off to work. Run away, is more like it. Stephanie spent the night at a girlfriend's house. At least she didn't go through the terror we did. It's one thing for it to terrorize me, but if it ever affects her, that's on a whole new level. I know Jeff won't allow it. Although Jeff has had plenty of his own strange experiences, they aren't as terrifying as mine. Even when I blew him away with proof, he still doesn't believe in the existence of anything paranormal. In my opinion, he will always be a skeptic. Sometimes it drives me crazy, and makes me feel even more isolated and alone, but until he actually sees a ghost *or a monster* with his own eyes . . . I'm screwed.

~

As soon as Jeff leaves for work, I'm going to take a shower and check out Oracle. It's the metaphysical store the girl who works at the Christian bookstore referred me to. She highly recommended it, especially after she witnessed the priest turn me down cold. I could tell by the look on her face it surprised her. Obviously, she never had to attend Catholic school. *Lucky girl.*

I finished my shower free from any paranormal experiences this morning, thank God. I used to love taking showers. Not anymore. I'm so paranoid of something happening again, so I take the fastest shower I possibly can. Just in and out. I'm especially afraid of the shower off the main bedroom, even though I've had terrifying experiences in both. At least today was calm.

I was almost done drying my hair when I began feeling uneasy and somewhat panicked. This is ridiculous, I'm just freaking myself out. I'm so paranoid lately that something is about to happen. I need to stop this. I don't want my fears to become a self-fulfilled prophecy. I think it will be great for me to get out of this house for a while. Maybe I will take myself out for lunch somewhere after I visit Oracle. I just need to take a deep breath and try to relax.

I could really use a break.

I finished drying my hair. I unplugged the blow dryer, wrapped it up and bent down to put it away in the cupboard under the sink. As I stood up and looked in the mirror, something in the mirror directly behind me caught my eye. The mirrors in our master bathroom face each other, thus creating an "infinity mirror." The reason they're called infinity mirrors is because they create an infinite number of reflections.

The number of reflections is infinite when two mirrors are perfectly parallel to one another, as with the mirrors in our bathroom.

Today as I looked in the mirror behind me, I saw what appeared to be a man dressed in a black suit walking toward me through each section of the mirror. He slowly and deliberately walked through each mirror image as if he were walking through different dimensions. Every time he passed into a different section, I could see a flicker of light shining within the mirror as if a door was being opened and shut behind him. This reflected off the edge of the mirror through each section. As he moved closer toward the end, a different colored light reflection moved with him. His movements appeared very methodical, yet robotic. He didn't move like a normal person. It was the most fascinating and terrifying thing I've ever witnessed. It mesmerized me. His eyes were staring directly into mine and I stood there completely transfixed. He smiled at me in such a strange way, I couldn't tell if he was friendly or sinister. I couldn't move, it felt as if my feet were anchored to the floor. A second later it hit me . . . whatever this is, it's not human and it's definitely not friendly. Beyond my fear, I remembered to pray. Instinct kicked in and I knew my only hope was to pray.

Please God, help me break free. Please get me out of here before this thing walks out of the mirror and kills me. Please, in the name of Jesus, help me!!

The prayer worked and I broke free. I ran out of there so freaking fast. Thank God I got out before he reached the end. I was scared to death he'd either kill me or worse, pull me back inside the mirror with him. Since I'm so used to doubting myself, here I go again. I've been accused of having an overactive imagination, could I have just imagined it? No way, I know what I saw. I couldn't have imagined this, not in a million years.

This was 100% real.

The scariest part was, I know for a fact that every single house in our neighborhood has the same mirrors in their master bathrooms. Infinity mirrors throughout the entire neighborhood. I've heard mirrors can be a portal to other dimensions. Could a neighborhood full of infinity mirrors create infinite portals into our world? It makes perfect sense to me. Its mind blowing and truly terrifying. Just in case my house wasn't scary enough, I just got to witness a creepy man walking through the mirror in my bathroom. Plus, now I have a cool new thing to worry about. I just pray that someday I can find someone who will help me make some sense out of all of this.

In my haste to get out of the house, I forgot to tie my shoes. As I was running into the garage to get in my car and drive away, I tripped on my shoelace and fell flat on my face on the concrete floor. I slowly got up and sat down on the step to tie my shoes. I heard some laughter from inside the house as soon as I finished tying them. I felt some blood dripping down my face, but no way was I going back inside for a first aid kit. I just wiped the blood off with my shirt and got in the car. I was so shook-up and intent on getting out of there, I almost drove right through the garage door without opening it first. I'm a little too frazzled to drive, so I'm going to just sit on the side of the road for a while.

I drove about a block away from my hell house before I pulled over. I turned off the engine while taking some deep breaths in to calm myself down. I sat there for what seemed like mere seconds when someone tapped on my window.

It was just a neighbor out walking her dog.

"Julie, are you alright?"

"Yes, Jackie, I'm fine. Just feeling a little shaky, so I thought it best to sit here until it passes."

"Oh, you too, huh? You got issues with your house? Ghosts perhaps? Do you want to talk about it?"

Yes, as a matter of fact, I do.

"You too, Jackie? OMG, I'm so desperate to talk to someone about it. Want to go get some coffee and chat?"

Jackie didn't answer me. I looked back over to my left where she was standing and she had completely disappeared. What the hell? How was she just there a second ago, and now she's gone?

Suddenly, a car stops next to me and toots their horn. I look over to see it's Jeff.

"Hey Jeff, what are you doing coming home already?"

"I was coming home for lunch, why are you parked on the side of the road."

"I'm not sure. I must have fallen asleep."

"Well, you definitely shouldn't be driving. Maybe you should come home and take a nap."

Problem is, I'm too afraid to go home. I must have been so tired when I pulled over, I fell fast asleep and didn't even know it. Jackie was never there. That must have been just another one of my wild dreams. That, or I'm losing my mind.

"Well, Julie, are you coming home or not?"

I don't want to go back home, and I really didn't want to tell him about what happened in the bathroom this morning. I especially didn't want to talk about it inside the house.

"If you don't mind, I need to go run some errands."

"Alright, have it your way. See you tonight."

I looked down at my watch before taking off and to my amazement, two hours had already passed. I must be more exhausted than I realized. I was relieved Jeff let me go. I desperately needed a break from our house. I also need to find someone who can help me. As I drove out of the neighborhood, I started thinking about my most recent paranormal experiences when a thought came to me. First was the knocking at the door, then came my horrific dream that left actual blood on the wall, and the scariest one of all, the man walking through the mirror. The experiences themselves happened in a set of three. I don't remember how much time passed between each experience, I wouldn't be surprised if they were three hours apart. The weirdest thing about the first experience was the fact that the knocking began at exactly 3:33 in the morning. Too many "threes" to be a coincidence. My first paranormal trifecta. I don't even know if such a thing exists, but it does now.

Another shocking thing I've learned is the sweet little girl running in and out of our coat closet wasn't a sweet little girl after all. It was a demon wanting us to think she was a sweet little girl. I guess if you're a scary monster, what better way to lure unsuspecting innocent people in. *It's diabolical.* I truly believed it was just a harmless little girl spirit. I will definitely need help to rid myself of that little monster. All I can do at this point is pray I will get the answers I need someday. I'm putting a lot of hope into this new store called Oracle. I'm not much for metaphysical or new age stores, but if they can help me, more power to them. I will become a fan real fast.

I daydreamed all the way to Oracle. I don't even remember how I got there. It's scary when you can daydream as well as I can. I'm driving down the road, but my mind is elsewhere. Am I even consciously aware of other cars? I really don't have a clue. I must have angels watching over me when I drive. This is ridiculous, I really need to pay better attention. My mind is too overwhelmed with the paranormal these days.

I pulled into Oracle's parking lot. It didn't look anything like what I anticipated. I expected it to be something like Woodstock, with hippies dancing around the front yard in long fabric sarongs draped around their semi-naked bodies. This was nothing like that at all. It was very inviting and looked like it used to be someone's home. As I walked up to the door, I smelled a familiar scent that brought me so much peace in the past. It's the scent of lavender. My grandma's bathroom was all purple and always smelled like lavender. This gave me a sense of calm, a sense of peace before I even walked in the front door. There was a beautiful courtyard with a waterfall and unique plants growing out of the rocks. Very tranquil and lovely. This just felt right to me.

I walked up to the door, but before I could open it, a lady on the other side opened the door and welcomed me in.

"Welcome to Oracle. Is this your first time here?"

"Yes, it is thank you."

"Feel free to walk around and if there's anything I can help you with, please don't hesitate to ask."

"There is something I came here for."

Suddenly, this fear came over me and I hesitated to tell her the reason I was there. Instead, I chickened out and made up an excuse.

"I'm looking for some sage. Do you sell sage?"

"Yes, as a matter of fact we do. We burn it like crazy around here, can you smell it? We just burned some this morning."

"I think so, it smells a little like pot to me."

"Yep, that's the sage. If you don't care for the smell, there are other things I can recommend."

"No, sage is fine. I just don't remember the sage I've burned at my house smelling this strong before."

"There are many varieties of sage, some stronger than others. We burn sage to keep the negative energies out, and the positive energies in."

"Here's our selection of sage. We also sell abalone shells and smudge feathers."

"Interesting. Why abalone shells?"

"We use abalone shells as a tool for smudging. The shell represents the water element and is a gift from the sea. The unlit herbs represent earth, the lit herbs represent fire, and the smoke represents air. The shell is useful as a bowl to catch hot cinders that might fall and holds the rest of the smudging stick when it's done being burned."

"Wow, that's interesting. What about the feather? What's the feather used for and is there any significance to it?"

"The feather is used to fan the smoke around a space that is being cleared of negative energy. In Native cultures birds are highly revered. They are also called, 'prayer fans.' The feather is made from a variety of different birds, here we have a blessed Indian prayer fan made from an eagle feather. The feather aids in the positive cleansing of a person's energy or aura and helps to remove blockages. It's a wonderful tool as a cleansing smoke bath. We have a Native American Navajo hand-made sacred prayer feather I could recommend for you. Very powerful."

"Wow, you are very knowledgeable. I'm still new to all this and to be honest, it's my first time in your store."

"Well dear, I could tell that when you walked in. Please share with me why you are really here and what we can do to help you. I had a feeling there was a lot more to you than what you're telling me. Don't worry, you are safe here. We don't judge, we only want to help improve your journey. I fear something is troubling you."

Suddenly, with no warning, I felt this overwhelming need to cry. I just stood there in the middle of the store, unable to speak with tears streaming down my face. I had absolutely no control over it. I remember this happened to me in church once. I left the Catholic faith and started attending a non-denominational Christian church. I was listening to the sermon when suddenly, an overwhelming urge to cry overcame me. I felt so embarrassed and had no clue what was happening to me. A lady seated next to me in the pew leaned over and asked me if I needed anything.

"I'm ok. I just don't understand what's happening to me. I can't stop crying."

She smiled at me as if she knew exactly what was going on.

"The Holy Spirit touched your heart. When our hearts are touched by the Holy Spirit, we simply can't resist the urge to cry."

She was a lovely woman. She taught me a lot about faith and how it wasn't necessary to fear God, like they had taught me in Catholic school. She told me God wants to have a relationship with us, God is forgiving, and there's no need to fear him. I became a Christian and gave my soul to Jesus at that very moment.

Standing in the middle of this "new age" type of store felt very much the same to me. I felt like I was being touched by the Holy Spirit. At that moment, I knew I was exactly where I needed to be. It felt life changing in ways I couldn't understand. In a million years I never would have expected anything like this, but it gave me so much peace.

I finally calmed down enough to apologize.

"I don't know what came over me."

She understood and told me it happened to her the first time she came here, too.

"This is a healing place, cry all you need to."

The wave of tears hit me all over again.

After I calmed back down, she asked me to tell her why I was really there.

"What's troubling you, dear?"

"I think my home is haunted."

"Yes, I sensed something might be attached to you. I know we can help you. Have you tried to reach out to anyone else for help?"

"Don't get me started. I tried to get a priest to come bless our house again, and he refused. He would only give me holy water and blessed salt. I've tried my best to bless the house myself. I really don't know what I'm doing. I'm having very vivid and terrifying dreams. I had a paranormal group come to do an investigation, and they never called me back. I know our house is haunted. I've already seen and heard many different spirits. We even have one that mimics our voices."

"That can be very dangerous, dear. Have you considered moving?"

"Yes, and no. We love the house. We've only lived there a short time. Besides, how can I, in good conscious, sell a house when there might be something wrong with it? How can you do that to some unsuspecting person? That's the primary reason I'm here. I desperately need some help. I'm feeling like I don't know what to do anymore. Nothing I've tried is working."

She gave me the warmest hug.

"You poor girl, we can help you. I know we can. You stay strong and don't let any of those nasty spirits push you around, you hear? You are more powerful than any of them."

She had the most soothing Jamaican accent. I could listen to her talk for hours.

"From what I've described, what do you think is happening?"

"You could have something attached to you, would be my best guess. I believe a lot more investigating needs to be done. We have mediums here that can probably tap into what's going on and help you. Have you ever experienced anything paranormal before?"

"No, not since I was sixteen."

"Well, if you've experienced it once, chances are good you'll experience it again."

Terrific.

She recommended one of their psychic mediums, and I made an appointment without hesitation. What I didn't realize at the time was that this visit was significant. This would be the first day of my spiritual journey. I believe my soul felt it, even if I didn't know it yet.

I purchased my sage kit with the abalone shell and blessed Indian eagle feather, thanked her for her help and left. When I walked out the door, I had a sense that I was exactly where I needed to be. Even though talking about the paranormal was uncomfortable for me, I felt peaceful for the first time in a very long time. Not just that, I was feeling hopeful that I was finally going to get the help I so desperately needed. I didn't realize just how much walking through those doors was going to help me get to the truth about a lot of things. Not just the activity in my house, this is going to change my life. I can hardly wait until tomorrow when I get to meet one of their counselors for the very first time.

22

Walking back into Oracle felt like home. I had a peaceful night last night, so I'm feeling refreshed and ready to understand whatever is going on. I'm nervous, but I won't let that stop me. I had lots of paperwork to fill out. The visit with the medium wasn't cheap. However, it gave me a full hour and I have a feeling I'm going to need it. I didn't know what to expect. I was both nervous and excited at the same time. I just hope she's the real deal. I've gone to others in the past that were absolute frauds and only out to separate me from my money.

I'm sitting in the waiting room, nervously waiting for them to call me. Part of me wants to leave, but the other part is telling me to stay. There's a definite battle going on inside my head. Frankly, I'm surprised the price of the visit didn't give me an excuse to leave. I believe some force in the Universe made me stay in my chair and patiently wait to hear my name. Never in a million years could I have prepared myself for what was about to happen.

"Julie Coons?"

I stood up and raised my hand.

"Right here."

I got up and walked into a room that looked like it was once someone's bedroom. It was dark yet inviting. There were two overstuffed couches on each side of the room. The only light came from one small table lamp and two Himalayan salt lamps.

The lady reached out to shake my hand.

"Hi, I'm Theresa. Please have a seat on the couch."

I was instantly at ease with Theresa. She sat on the couch opposite me. She said nothing to me at first. Instead, she closed her eyes for a few seconds. When she opened them back up, I saw her look up to the corner of the room as if she were looking at someone hovering in midair. It was fascinating.

"Give me a second, I'm tapping into your spirit guides and consulting with my guide Kia, who's here in the room with us."

I'm getting goosebumps.

She explained that she's fairly new at this, so she's still receiving help from her own guide. I fully expected her to ask me why I was there, but she didn't need to. I'm guessing I really do have spirit guides who are communicating for me. This really is amazing. It's so far beyond my comprehension, but I was extremely intrigued.

A moment later, Theresa put her left hand on her upper stomach area. With an incredibly compassionate look on her face, she looked over at me and said, "Unspeakable pain."

The only words I could choke out were, "Shut up!"

I'm a little embarrassed I told her to shut up, but she absolutely blew my mind. There's no way she could have known I suffered from pancreatitis. The most amazing part was when she placed her hand exactly in the same location where I feel the most pain when I'm having a flare-up. I believe she did that to validate to me she was the real deal and not a fraud. I listened to everything she said and had no reason not to believe her. She had me on the edge of my seat. I sat in complete amazement of her.

She sat silent for a few more minutes, then she had something else incredible to say.

"I'm getting that you need to write a book."

That was the last thing I expected her to say.

"I need to write a book? Who said I need to write a book?"

"I'm getting information from your spirit guides. They are telling me you have quite an amazing story to tell."

I didn't even need to ask. I believe she was referring to my abusive childhood.

"No way. I'm not a writer and frankly, I don't want to relive any part of my past. No, thank you. That's never going to happen."

"Julie, you really should think about it. I'm also being told you could help others heal their own pain through your story."

Crap!

Why did she have to say that? Now I feel obligated. Problem was, how do I say no to my spirit guides? I don't want to write that book, and I don't know the first thing about writing a book. I didn't love English class in high school. I wanted to be a doctor, not an author. I never intended to write anything, let alone a book.

"Are you sure you're getting that message correctly? Why would my spirit guides think for one second I even had the ability to do that?"

"I'm only sharing the message I'm getting and they are adamant about it. They are showing me your story in lights on the silver screen."

Now she's delusional.

"Really? Someone is going to make a movie about my life?"

"That's what I'm getting. I'm told it's an incredible story about how you survived your childhood. You also escaped an abusive husband. Is that true? You saved yourself and your daughter?"

"I did."

Holy crap, she's good.

"Julie, I encourage you to just think about it. Your spirit guides aren't just blowing smoke. They are trying to guide you to your path. This is the message they are giving me. The way to your future. Please, just think about it."

"Ok, I will. I'm just incredibly shocked right now. I expected nothing like this to happen today."

"I get that a lot."

Then she laughed the most contagious laugh I've ever heard. She has such kind eyes and a genuine way about her. I was completely at ease with her the moment we met.

"Do what you want and if it's too painful, then don't put yourself through it. I'm just giving you the message I'm getting. It's up to you to act on it. We have some time left. Do you have any questions for me? Are there any issues you'd like to discuss?"

"Yes, I do. I'm not sure how to begin. Should I just start at the beginning?"

"Whatever you like."

"We moved into our brand-new home a few months ago. It was new construction and we are the first owners. I don't understand how a new home can be haunted, but ours seems to be."

I explained everything to Theresa, beginning with the red writing on the mantle, the mimicking of our voices, right up to the events of a couple nights ago. I was afraid I would freak her out, but she didn't seem a bit surprised.

"You're telling me about the current paranormal events you're experiencing in your new home now, but have you really gone back far enough in your history? Are there any previous paranormal experiences you've had prior to the most recent ones?"

"Well, it's a long story."

"Better get going on it then."

"Well, I almost died when I was fifteen. I left my body and came back."

"Did it feel like you were being pushed back into your body?"

"YES!!"

Wow, nobody else has ever asked me that question. Most people don't even believe me, so I stopped talking about it.

"Julie, at what age did you see your first spirit?"

She just blew my mind, *again*.

"When I was sixteen."

"What did you see?"

"A Civil War soldier."

Theresa calmly responded, "That's very common. When a medium starts to see spirits, their first one is usually a Civil War soldier."

"I'm a medium?"

"Yes, and a very gifted one at that."

Again, I've got nothing better to respond with than, "shut up!"

Theresa laughed again. "It's a rare gift you have. Spirits know you can see them, and they are attracted to you because of it. I'm surprised you're not bothered more. I'm hearing from your spirit guides that you're a very gifted medium."

"Is it because of my near-death experience?"

"I'm getting the out-of-body episode brought you very close to the veil and heightened your abilities, but you somehow shut them down. You were born a medium. I believe it's passed down and is also multi-generational. Most likely through the women in your family on your mother's side."

"That makes sense."

I was wrapping my head around this new knowledge enough to look back a little.

"My mother predicted my grandma was going to die within hours of her death. We were supposed to go to her house for dinner. I was outside playing with my friends on the sidewalk in front of our house. Mom was working in the yard and called me over to her. I noticed she was crying. When I asked what was wrong, she told me something bad was going to happen to Grandma and we wouldn't be going to her house that night for dinner."

"Wow, that's a heavy load to put on a child. How old were you?"

"Six."

"I've also gotten some intense information about your mom. She had a nasty habit of putting you and your brother in adult situations. I also got that she abused you."

"Yes."

"Is she responsible for you nearly dying? What's the story behind that?"

"Well, I had a kidney infection. As the afternoon progressed my symptoms got worse. I begged her to get me to my doctor, and she ignored me. Later that night around 9:00 when my father came home from work, he arrived in time to hear me fall off the toilet. I had fainted. My father is the one who took me to the emergency room."

"So, you and your mother don't have a good relationship?"

"Not at all."

"You broke the cycle of abuse for your daughter. That's remarkable and something few people accomplish. Good for you, Julie. No wonder the spirits want you to write a book."

Ugh!

"What about your grandma on your mother's side? Did she have any abilities you know of?"

"No idea, I never really knew my grandma. I only got to meet her when I was sixteen and by then the doctor had diagnosed her with Alzheimer's disease."

"So sorry to hear that. Why didn't you know your grandma? Did she live far away or something?"

"No, my grandparents lived about ten minutes away from us my entire life. My aunt told me they lived across the street from the Catholic grade school I attended. If they knew what we looked like they could have most likely watched us playing on the playground."

"That's horrible. Why didn't you have a relationship with them?"

"Mom wouldn't allow it. I guess she was punishing them or something. I really felt robbed from having grandparents. My grandfather on my father's side died before I was born, and Grandma Eva died when I was six. The one set I had, I wasn't allowed to have a relationship with."

"Your mother sounds like a piece of work."

"That's putting it nicely."

"Before you go, I have just one more question."

"Ok, but don't expect an intelligent answer, I'm mentally trashed."

"Why did you shut down your abilities when you were sixteen? You could read auras in multiple shades and you were really beginning to grow. By the way, your spirit guides are telling me, you're not just a medium, you're an empathic medium just like I am. The spirits showed me a mirror which indicates to me we are mirror images of each other. We have very similar abilities and similar stories. I was also abused as a child."

"I was too afraid my friends would find out. My friends were everything to me in high school. I couldn't risk them finding out I can see dead people. They would think I was nuts and stop being friends with me. I couldn't take that risk. I'm also very sorry you were abused."

"Did you notice all three Himalayan salt lamps have stayed lit the entire time you've been here?"

"No, I didn't notice."

"I just wanted to let you know, that's all because of your energy. These are special salt lamps that either light up or don't. It's entirely affected by your energy. Isn't that cool?"

I think she just wanted to blow my mind one last time before I left.

"Before I go, how do I deal with all the activity in my home? Also, could there be a demon in my house? There's so much more I need to talk to you about."

"Would you like to make another appointment?"

"Absolutely."

"I have time right now, would you like to keep talking?"

"I would, but I'm exhausted. I think I need to go home, re-energize and come back another day."

"Before you go, I want you to know you're in control. There's nothing the spirit world can do to you. You have the power to stand up to it. The entities in your home are most likely feeding off your energy and especially your fear. Don't allow it. Burn your sage, say a prayer and order the negative energy to leave. It's really all about intention. Set an intention with the spirit world and mean it. You also need to set some strict boundaries so they stop waking you up at all hours of the night."

"Theresa, can they get into my dreams and give me nightmares?"

"It's easier for the spirit world to communicate with us through our dreams because our minds are the most open, so yes."

"How do I not be so afraid? The things that happen in my home scare the crap out of me."

"Just remember what I told you. Once you set some boundaries and make an intention and stick to it, things will quickly improve. Remember, you're the one who's alive, not them. They don't have the power to hurt you."

"Thanks Theresa, I will do my best."

"I believe there was a reason we were put together. I'm so glad I got to meet you. Now you go home and get some rest. You're going to need it. Don't worry, in time this will all make sense to you. See you later."

Our session was over, I was exhausted and ready to go home. It felt like all the energy got sucked out of me. It was only an hour appointment, but it felt like so much longer. A lot of information to take in, in such a short amount of time. She's right, I really have a lot to think about.

I'm not so sure I believed everything she said about all the power I supposedly possess. I believe that has more to do with my poor self-esteem, though. It's hard for me to think of myself as gifted or powerful. Kind of cool to think about, I guess, but it's going to take some time. I'm too exhausted to care right now.

23

Meeting with Theresa was a profound experience. She told me I'm gifted. I'm still struggling to understand it all. I never felt gifted in anything, let alone things associated with the paranormal. I'm not so sure I even want this gift. How is it a gift if it terrifies you? So much of what she told me is still a bit of a blur. In my defense, what she said completely shocked me. Theresa told me, "You have a rare ability to see and actually communicate with these entities. You don't have to be tormented by it." Can I truly embrace my gift and make peace with it? I'm not so sure at this point in time.

It really was a relief to find someone who can help me understand something that seemed impossible to comprehend. It wasn't just our home, it's me. I attract the energy as if I'm a beacon of light for the spirit world. Not everyone has the same experiences and abilities that I do. Theresa said it's very rare to see disembodied spirits as full-bodied and solid like I can. She told me, "it will take time for you to fully embrace your gift." She also said the energy that's attracted to me, stays with me. Moving would not stop this. It's overwhelming to understand this is my fate. One thing I'm sure of, this meeting with Theresa is going to change the course of my life.

Understanding is one thing, but dealing with it's another. I still have no clue how to deal with all the activity in our home. If I caused it, then I should have the power to put an end to it, right?

I need a break from all of this. I'm driving myself crazy. I really wish I'd gotten to know my mother's mom better. She's gone now. Her name was Clarice. I wonder if Clarice knew there were spirits around me since I was very young. These abilities are passed down through the women of the family, according to Theresa. From mother to daughter, grandmother to granddaughter, and it seems to grow stronger throughout the generations. I wish my grandma had helped me understand how to navigate my abilities at a younger age. My mother wanted no part of it, even though she had abilities of her own. My parents stopped me from talking about it as a child in a pretty intense way.

"If you ever talk about this again, we will commit you to an insane asylum and you will never see your friends again."

Mom did everything in her power to make me believe I was crazy. She mocked me, then she forbade me from ever speaking of it again.

My parents knew my friends meant everything to me. They threatened me into silence. I was too afraid to tell anyone. I couldn't risk my friends thinking I was some kind of freak, either. As a child I didn't understand my abilities, so I feared them. I had a lot of anxiety because of it. I felt very isolated and alone. Nobody taught me how to manage the fear. I just wish someone would have been honest with me and told me the truth. I was different, but that didn't make me bad. My parents were very strict disciplinarians. My father used to say, "I'm going to put the fear of God into you." I never really knew what that meant, but I knew it wasn't good. They would get so angry and out of control when they punished us. There were times I feared I was in jeopardy of losing my life. I had frequent nightmares about my mother grabbing a knife and killing me. This was no joke to me as a kid. My parents ruled with an iron fist and as a result, their children feared them.

Maybe my abilities are a blessing and a curse. I struggle to think of it as a gift. Before talking to Theresa, I wondered if I was going crazy. I questioned if all the paranormal stuff was actually happening. Now I know it really IS happening. At least I'm not feeling so alone and hopeless anymore. That is a dangerous place to be mentally. I've always struggled with self-confidence. I'm wondering if self-doubt could make me more vulnerable to evil entities that only want to manipulate, control, and eventually possess their victims.

Now my mind is getting out of control and I really need to stop thinking about this. I will talk to Theresa next time I see her. Today, I need to take my time cleansing my home with the intention of bringing peace to it once and for all. I still have so much more to learn before this is over. Until I get the help I need from Theresa and learn how to deal with everything, I need to lay low and try not to cause any more activity.

Now, will someone please tell me how to accomplish that . . .

Another task I need to look into is how to clean the red markings off the wood in the hallway. I have no idea how the entity in my dream popped out of my head and turned the clear slime in the hallway into a red substance, but they did. I don't know what the red substance is, but I have my suspicion. Pretty sure it's blood. I think the red marking on the mantle was also blood. Or, whatever this is, intended it to look like blood.

One thing I know for sure, that little girl running around our house is no sweet, innocent little ghost girl. I believe she's a demon mimicking a little girl. Another thing Theresa told me is demons often present as sweet little girls. I will deal with my demonic little angel another time. Hopefully she had her fun and will leave me alone for a while.

I need to get rid of the red mystery glob running down the wainscoting in the hallway. I just can't look at that wall another day. Every time I walk down the hallway, it freaks me out.

Nothing was cleaning it off. I tried every trick I knew, just like on the mantle above the fireplace, and it wasn't budging. This stuff was a little thicker than the substance on the mantle, but looked very similar. It's so creepy how this came to be. If I took it to a scientist in a lab, could they tell me what this substance is? *Doubt it.* I sense it most likely came from another dimension. I wouldn't be surprised if the scientific community never saw a substance like it before. Jeff certainly wouldn't fork out the money for an analysis. There's no way anyone can tell me what this is. Worse, the information could reach the media and we would look like the freak shows of the neighborhood. I won't be telling anyone about this. Some things are better left unsaid.

We had no other choice but to rip out all the wainscoting, and then we burned it. As it burned, it gave off the worst stench. It was like sulfur, sewage and rotting flesh all mixed together. It was incredibly disgusting and putrid. Then it started smelling like vomit. I had to walk away to get some fresh air. It was so gross it made me gag. I'm surprised I didn't puke. While it was burning, we saw plumes of black smoke rising high in the air, then it dove straight down as if it were drilling deep into the ground. From there, I didn't want to know where it ended up. My imagination might have been working overtime, but I thought it shot back down straight to hell where it came from. Part of me fears I'm right.

Jeff and I repaired the wall ourselves. We didn't want to hire a contractor for fear our big secret would get out. As soon as we completed our work, I decided it was time to sit down with Jeff and tell him all about my meeting with Theresa. I hadn't told him I'd gone to see a medium yet. I'm still a little apprehensive to tell him about it. He has a right to know, but I'm fearful of how he's going to react. I have a feeling I already know what the biggest skeptic in the world is going to think. I was right, he discounted everything I told him as total nonsense.

"Whatever. So now you think you're a witch?"

"Yeah Jeff, exactly. You figured me out, I'm a witch."

Jerk.

Why does he have to be such a skeptic? Why does he have to question every single thing? I'm so annoyed with him right now. I get that I'm naïve, but Theresa validated her abilities to me. It was mind blowing how much she knew about me, especially since we'd never even met before.

"Julie, don't fall for that crap. Those people have ways to find out stuff about you. You probably gave away information without even knowing it."

Those people, what an insult.

"No way, Jeff. She told me about my pancreatitis pain. She even held her hand on the same spot where my pain is. It was the first thing she said to me."

"Well, I guess I can't quite explain that, but I'm sure there's an easy explanation for how she found out. She obviously researched you before you came in. She probably called the hospital to ask if you've ever been a patient there."

"Ok, first, that's confidential information and second, she didn't even know my name before she met me."

Riddle me that genius.

"Julie, please don't be so naïve."

Fighting words.

"Jeff, I don't want to talk to you about this anymore. I'm sorry I even said anything."

"Julie, don't get mad. I know you're stressed about everything that's happened lately. I'm sure we will solve it someday. We'll probably even have a good laugh when we do."

"Jeff, why won't you believe me? You've even had some paranormal experiences yourself. How in the world do you still not believe? It drives me crazy how much you continue to doubt this."

The drive gets shorter and shorter . . .

"I'm sure there's a reasonable explanation that doesn't include the paranormal."

"Sure, like the time you heard my voice calling your name when I wasn't even home. How do you "reasonably" explain that?"

"Who knows, maybe I imagined it, or I could have been dreaming it, whatever. What I know is that you're driving yourself nuts trying to figure it all out."

"Never mind, Jeff. I'm sorry I even said anything."

I was getting angry, so I ended the conversation and walked away. I didn't want this to drive another wedge between us. I guess I will go back to the way it was and just deal with this all by myself. I'm still going to see Theresa no matter what he says. I will just see her secretly. I know she was telling me the truth. There's no way she did any research. She got all the information about me directly from my spirit guides. I intuitively knew she was telling me the truth.

Maybe someday Jeff will believe.

Regardless, this is my journey and mine alone. I guess that's the message here. Nobody is going to walk it with me. That made me feel a little sad. It would sure be nice to feel like I had a partner in all of this. But I don't and that's that. I believe Jeff is just fearful of the things he doesn't understand. That explains me perfectly. I'm the thing he's struggling to understand. Well, get on board, sir. This is my life and now you're in it. You can turn your back on the facts, but someday you might not have that luxury. I can't exactly foretell the future, but I'm fearful things are only going to get worse.

The strangest part was, when Jeff and I weren't getting along, it really seemed to intensify the activity in the house. I think whatever is here not only feeds on fear, it really likes anger, too. I had to stop the argument to protect ourselves against anything happening. I feel like we are constantly being watched and listened to. I also feel like I have to be careful not to give it too much attention. That also ramps up activity. One thing I'm certain of, this thing feeds off our energy. I believe fear gives it the most power, so that's why it's constantly trying to scare me. I must really empower it. I need to stop being so afraid. How in the world am I supposed to accomplish that? I'm afraid of everything.

~

I needed to get away from the house for a while, so I took a walk. There's so much of my new town I haven't explored yet. I just need to take a long walk and clear my head. There's a beautiful untouched forest area down the road. I think it's time to go hiking and explore a little. It's a lovely Saturday afternoon. I don't have any errands to run, and I didn't have to worry about picking Stephanie up from school.

"Jeff, can you keep an eye on Stephanie for a while? I'm going to take a walk."

"Yeah, sure."

It's the perfect day for a hike. I felt lighter and increasingly more relaxed as I walked further and further away from our house. Lately, I've been feeling much more at ease whenever I'm away from home.

Conversely, when I am driving back down our street toward home is when the anxiety comes flooding back. It's terrible how much I prefer not to be at home. It's become a new normal for me. I've never experienced this before. It's heartbreaking how much my semi-new home has become my worst nightmare. We've lived here almost nine months now. The winter is almost over and the ground is finally warming up. I hate the winter. I live for summer. Because I have Fibromyalgia, I ache more in the winter. I have complete freedom from fibro pain in the summer. I really need to live in the desert where it's warm and dry.

About a mile from our house is the wooded area I've been wanting to explore ever since we moved here. It's so odd to find an area like this mixed in with modern housing developments. Jeff grew up in this town. He told me the entire area used to be part of this forest. I grew up in another town that had a similar forest area on the outskirts of my neighborhood and right next to my old high school. My friends and I frequently hung out there. We called it, "Sherwood Forest." The kids who partied also hung out there, but my friends and I weren't part of their group. We called them, "Hoods."

As I wander through my new town's version of Sherwood Forest, I'm very much reminded of the old days. This area looks very similar to what I remember. It's a lot bigger than what we had, so I will have to be careful not to get lost. I find walking through the forest to be a mystical experience. I like to look at all the different types of plant life and hoped I'd maybe even see a forest animal. I feel so peaceful in the forest. I'd only been exploring a few minutes when I came upon a dirt pathway. It quite intrigued me and I wondered where it might lead to, so I followed it. It's also a good idea to stay on a path, especially since I'm not familiar with the area. It will hopefully keep me from getting lost.

I was surprised to notice a few small homes sprinkled around as I walked along the dirt path. I had no idea there were any homes in this area. They didn't look like they belonged here. Who builds houses in the middle of a forest? This entire area is forest land with a dirt pathway down the middle. They look like they're straight out of the fifties. There weren't any roads leading to any of these houses either, so I'm not sure how or why they were even built here. *Strange, I thought.* This was a far cry from the upscale neighborhood I lived in next door. Most of the homes had thick brush growing up the side and over the roof, as if the land was trying to swallow them back up. I'm guessing these homes were abandoned a long time ago. Maybe that's why I can't find any roads leading to any of them. Now I'm wondering why they're abandoned. It all felt so weird to me. I felt like I was transported inside a fairy tale and little red riding hood was about to come out of one of the houses. It seemed like I had walked into another dimension as soon as I stepped foot inside the forest. It was that strange and unreal walking through there. I only saw three homes, but the whole ambience of this odd forest . . . to this day I still find it extremely mystifying.

Not nearly as freaky as what I was about to find, though.

As I walked a little further down the dirt path, I started getting a creepy feeling and felt like I was being watched. I even considered heading back home. However, curiosity got the better of me, so I kept walking. I felt a little like Dorothy in The Wizard of Oz when she followed the yellow brick road. Curiosity can be dangerous, I kept telling myself. *I heard it even killed a cat once.* I wanted to see where the path would lead to. I was becoming obsessed with it. Besides, I still needed more time away from Jeff. I'm afraid if I go back home too soon, we would start arguing again. Bad things happen in my home when the people in it are tense or fighting. That I know for a fact. I'm expecting some intense paranormal activity caused from the argument we had earlier. Fighting gives it power the same way fear does. It's really bizarre.

I've just reached the end of the path and I'm completely blown away at what I'm looking at. I'm standing in front of an old, abandoned looking cemetery. It's very overgrown with shrubbery, and I don't think anyone has tended to it in years. It really made me sad to see it in such a state of disrepair. I imagine over time the people who managed it eventually died, and it left no one to care for it. It looked as if time was swallowing it up. It's hard to tell how big this cemetery was because most of the headstones either disintegrated or went back into the earth. The headstones I could find were knocked over and weathered to the point of being illegible. I couldn't make out what any of them said.

It's surprising to find a cemetery deep in the middle of a predominately forested area. I've never seen or heard of anything like it. I wonder if the people buried here feel disrespected. I also wonder if this abandoned cemetery could have anything to do with the paranormal activity in my home. Is it just my home or are others in the neighborhood having similar experiences? I just don't have the guts to ask anyone that question. Just like back in high school, I can't risk my neighbors thinking I'm a freak.

I've got to get out of here. I said a prayer for the people buried in this bizarre cemetery, then I turned and walked away. I can't explain how creepy it feels to be alone in the middle of a forest and find an old abandoned cemetery. I'm especially bothered I couldn't see any dates carved on the few headstones that were still standing. Heaven knows how old it is. Also, why would anyone put a cemetery in the middle of the forest? That's just plain weird. I wonder if any of the homes I passed were associated with it. Maybe the people who lived there buried their deceased nearby in the cemetery. But these homes didn't look that old to me, they're not wood cabins like I'd expect to see if they were as old as that cemetery appeared.

I felt a sense of relief when I finally made it back to the main road. I felt like I had just entered another world. The sky seemed so bright once I made it out of the forest. It was dark when I walked a few feet inside it, and the deeper I went, the darker it became. Literally and figuratively. There was something strange about that forest. The fact that the path wasn't grown over like everything else was intriguing to me. Gravel had been poured over some of it. Maybe that's why there wasn't any shrubbery growing through it. Still, makes me wonder how long ago the gravel was poured and why. I've hiked a lot of paths before and rarely are they covered with gravel. Usually they are just dirt.

As I walked back home, I couldn't help but compare those abandoned homes to my next-door neighbors who moved out in the middle of the night. I wonder if there's a connection. Theresa said the activity is all because I'm supposedly a medium, but I feel if that's true it's only a small piece of the puzzle. If I truly am a medium, why can't I control it better? Why have my abilities subsided entirely until the moment we moved into this house? Why now and why this house? What is it about this area that makes me sense it's created some kind of spiritual Nexus? Is it me, or is it the land? I believe there's much more to the land our house is built on, maybe even the entire town. Another mystery yet to be solved. I think it's time I do a little more research.

24

I was right to be concerned about my argument with Jeff stirring up some paranormal activity. Something major was heading my way this time, but not in the manner I thought. I expected to get the crap scared out of me, and that didn't happen. Instead, it came as more of a message through a dream. Sometimes I can't really tell if my dreams are just that, or if it's a visit from spirit. Today I'm positive this was a visit from spirit. No doubt in my mind.

I arrived home from my walk to find Jeff and Stephanie had left. That's fine except they didn't leave me a note telling me where they went or when they'd be back. That's typical of Jeff when he's angry at me. Usually something like that would make me upset, but right now I don't care. I know Stephanie is safe and in excellent hands. I just would have appreciated a little consideration, that's all. I'm too tired to be angry and I don't need any more negative energy in this house. I'm already scared enough as it is.

I sat down on the couch and turned on my favorite television show. Within minutes, I fell asleep. In my dream I was talking to two fairly adolescent male Indian spirits.

"We are here in peace, do not be afraid."

When they finished speaking, they walked over to the coat closet and stood on each side as if they were guards.

"We are here to guide and protect you. There are two portals in your house coming in and out of this closet. We will protect it for you."

I always sensed there was a portal in there. This is the same coat closet I see that little demon girl running in and out of.

One portal was for the spirit world, and the other was a portal to hell.

"Demonic beings that were never from this earth are coming through the doorway in the closet."

They refer to portals as doorways.

"There is a thin spot between dimensions. Their draw to this location is two-fold. One, because something horrific happened here many years ago that cursed this land. Demonic entities are attracted to tragedy. The second, and more important reason is because they know you have abilities and you can see them. It only entices them more."

Incredible.

They warned me to find someone who could close the portals and rid them from my home before it's too late. They told me they were medicine men in life from a time long ago. I heard the word "shaman" for the first time from them. The Indian spirits told me they were risen from shamans in life to warriors fighting against evil in death.

"Your spirit guides brought us here to help you."

Hey, I will take all the help I can get whether it's from this world or not. They didn't scare me at all. I felt very much at peace with them. They told me they would stick around to help protect me and my family until I could find a way to close the portals. I felt so much better after talking to them.

"Next time you see us we will appear in the form of a shiny black panther. Do not be alarmed, we mean you no harm."

I instinctively knew they were good spirits and would watch over us. For the first time in months, I slept peacefully. This wasn't a dream at all, this was an actual visit from spirit.

Stephanie and Jeff came home and woke me out of my amazing dream. They were starving and more than a little annoyed I didn't have dinner ready for them yet. Jeff took Stephanie to her little league softball practice and stayed to help coach. How can I stay angry at a guy like that? He's good to Stephanie, and that's all that matters. Plus, Stephanie is flourishing in her new school.

Our move was good for everyone except me. For the most part, Jeff was oblivious to the paranormal activity. Even if he had experienced anything, *which he did*, he blew it off as something else. Stephanie had some experiences, but none as terrifying as mine. If she had been more affected or scared, there's no question we'd be out of here. It's one thing to terrorize me, but it had better lay off my child.

I thought it best to keep my forest adventure and dream to myself. Jeff has had about enough paranormal talk for one day and I really didn't want to cause another argument. I made my famous homemade macaroni and cheese dinner. We had a fun and relaxing evening, playing games and talking. We talked mostly about sports. Stephanie is a natural athlete. She will play little league softball this summer and start volleyball in the fall when she begins middle school. It was a wonderful stress-free evening. I desperately craved more nights like this, but unfortunately, they were few.

It'd been a long day. I was tired but also a little apprehensive when bedtime rolled around. I really dreaded falling asleep, especially lately. The nightmares have been terrifying except for this afternoon when I finally had a dream that didn't scare me half to death. Perhaps things are turning around. I sure hope so, I could really use a break.

It took little time to fall into a much-needed peaceful sleep, but unfortunately, the witching hour comes with its own set of issues. The witching hour, also known as the devil's hour, is 3 a.m. It's the time when the veil between the living and the dead is at its thinnest. I've had many dreams I've thought to be spiritual visits. I always assumed it's because we are more vulnerable and open when we are asleep. I've learned from Theresa *and my own research* that I was only partially correct. It's much easier for spirits to come to us in our dreams, but not only for the reason I was thinking.

First, we aren't preoccupied with the day-to-day activities of life

and we are much more open during sleep. There's a much big
reason, and it has to do with vibrational frequencies. Spirits hav
much higher vibrational frequency than we do because they are cl
than we are to the source of pure white light. Most of us on the pl
ical plane have a much lower vibrational frequency. Mediums
psychics naturally have a higher vibrational energy, and that is
it's easier for them to communicate with the spirit world. Howevei
nighttime when we are asleep, our vibrational frequency natur
changes. Sleep naturally puts us into a higher frequency.

Most people fall asleep long before 3 a.m., which puts us int
much deeper sleep. This raises our vibrational frequency even hig
to the level of the spiritual plane, thus making it much easier for
spirits to communicate with us inside our dream state.

I've also heard that it's possible to raise our vibrational freque
through meditation. Personally, I'm a little fearful to try meditati
I'm afraid of what I might attract or open myself up to. I've g
through life mostly on guard, and I'm too afraid to let my defer
down or become vulnerable. That's more than enough to scare
away. I've been told I could really benefit from meditation, but ma
some other time when I'm feeling stronger. I've got enough on
ever-growing plate.

Well, here we go again . . .

It's 3:00 in the morning and I hear three loud knocks at the fi
door. I shouldn't be surprised anymore, but it's incredibly startling
wake up this way in the middle of the night, especially out of a d
sleep.

I called 911. I didn't get up to answer the door this time, instea
sat quietly and waited for the police to show up. This time the offic
got here fast. Fast enough to see the person still standing on our fr
porch.

"Don't move and put your hands up."

The person at the door took his chances and ran instead.

When the officers reached him, he disappeared.

One officer was able to grab his coat in an effort to apprehend h
When he vanished, he left behind a small piece of blue fabric in
officer's visibly shaken hand.

"I swear, I had him and then suddenly he vanished. How the hell did that just happen?"

His eyes were as large as saucers.

"Even the piece of fabric disintegrated in the palm of my hand, right in front of my own eyes."

When the officer showed me what little he had left, I knew exactly what it was. I thought it looked like a small piece of heavy blue wool fabric. The same fabric used to make a coat or a uniform for a Civil War soldier. I knew it came from the soldier I saw at sixteen . . . my first spirit.

"See there, Officer? I'm really not crazy."

"Yeah, sure. But the problem is, now I think I'm losing it."

"Don't worry, Officer, sometimes there just isn't a logical explanation for these things."

I could see the poor officer was completely freaked out.

"Not in my world."

Oh yeah, imagine how big a skeptic a police officer must be.

"Well, thanks for coming out again, Officers. Have a lovely rest of your shift."

I walked back toward my house and left them standing in horror on my front lawn. What could I possibly say to them that would make any of this any easier?

As soon as I stepped back inside my home, I woke up. I could have sworn this dream was one hundred percent real. *That was too bizarre.* I sat up and tried to process it. This was the most vivid dream I've ever had. I even had to get up and look out the front window to make sure there really weren't two police officers standing on my lawn. Nothing was there. And now I know I'm losing my mind.

I got a drink of water and went back to bed. I fell right back asleep and continued to dream about my soldier. My dream took me back to a time when a battle was fought in our area. It was like I was watching a movie on a screen, but I was still inside my home. I walked outside the front door and something shining in the dirt caught my attention. I reached down and picked up a gold button lying in the flower beds. This was the same gold button I remember seeing on his double-breasted blue suit. Suddenly, I'm not inside my body anymore and I'm watching myself walk back inside the house. I wasn't alarmed or scared at all. I just felt like an observer. I followed behind and watched as I laid back down on the couch. The part of me that was outside of my body laid down on top of my body and then, I simply continued dreaming. Just another day in the life, I guess. When I try too hard to wrap my head around it, I just end up with a headache.

None of what happened seemed to bother me that much. It honestly felt like I instinctively knew my soul had left my body and it felt completely normal. As I look back on it, I find it freaky as hell, but at the time it felt like the most natural thing in the world.

I heard another knock at the front door. This time, instead of calling the police, I got up and answered it. I wasn't afraid anymore. I was more focused on how relieved I was to be back inside my body. When I opened the door, there he was. I was shocked to see my Civil War soldier standing there right in front of me. When our eyes met, I remembered how beautiful and brilliant his blue eyes were. I knew he was a spirit, but he presented to me as solid as a regular person. *It was incredible.* I relaxed a little and for the very first time I could speak to him. I just wish I would have said something other than what actually came out of my mouth.

"Why do you keep knocking on my door?" *Why did I say that? Couldn't I have just said hello?*

"Pardon me, Ma'am, I'm here looking for my girlfriend's father so I can ask for her hand in marriage."

Holy hell, he doesn't know he's dead.

At least I chose my words a little more carefully this time when I told him he's no longer alive. He lowered his head for a moment. When he looked back up at me, he was smiling. Then he said the most remarkable thing.

"Soldiers will always be here to remind people about what happened long ago so it's never forgotten."

He told me he died in battle and knew he was dead. He was here to pass on an important message.

"If we forget atrocities like the Civil War, there's a huge possibility history will repeat itself. Many soldiers I fought with, beside myself, are fearful this tragedy will occur again one day. That would be worse than losing a limb and eventually losing my own life."

"I will never forget you and I'm honored to share your story."

I truly believe there's an excellent reason these spirits are here. Their war will never truly end. Not because they're trapped souls, but because their stories will always need to be told. History won't go away, nor should it. We need to learn from the past to prevent it from ever happening again. It's a natural part of life between the living and the dead. The dead are here to teach us. They don't mean to frighten us, they just don't want us to make the same mistakes as our ancestors. He told me he was proud to die so history wouldn't repeat itself.

Such a courageous and honorable young man.

In my dream I saw a beautiful woman in a white wedding gown walking toward us. My soldier looked at me and smiled.

"Looks like she said yes."

I could barely speak. I was so choked up by what I was seeing. How blessed I felt to speak to my soldier and understand his purpose. I know now how important it is to remember the past. According to my soldier, we must never forget or it will doom us to repeat it. He didn't die in vain. I stood there in complete awe. My soldier gave me a wink and then turned away from me and walked toward his beautiful bride.

They walked hand in hand into a cloud of pure light.

I never saw my soldier again.

When I woke, I noticed I was holding onto something. I opened my hand and tucked safely inside my palm was a shiny gold button.

25

I will always treasure the visit from my spirit soldier. I know he was really here because now I have proof. I stared at my new shiny gold button in complete amazement. How is this even possible? How did an object from my dream morph into reality? I can't explain it to anyone, *especially not Jeff,* so I will just hide it for now and keep it to myself. It's difficult for me to keep a secret, especially one this big. However, Jeff and I are having issues and I doubt my shiny button will help anything. He will probably cart me off to the looney bin. Maybe that wouldn't be such a bad thing. I could really use a break.

I need to do some research. I've had some intense dreams from two Indians and now my soldier. These weren't just casual visits from spirit. This has to mean something more, and it's up to me to figure it out. Yes, my Indian spirits warned me to get some help to close the portals, but I also sense there's more to it. Why were they here to begin with? It gives me a sense of peace having them here and knowing they are protecting me. I want to learn more about them. I want to know what their story is. My intuition is telling me I need to look deeper, and that's exactly what I intend to do.

After I drove Stephanie to school, I went to our local library. I wasn't sure where to begin, so I went to their research desk. I got absolutely nowhere. They didn't even tell me about the rock crushing quarry that used to be where our lake is. I checked with City Hall and still, nothing. I even talked to a lady who claimed to be a historian of our area and again, nothing. She thought there may have been a car accident near our neighborhood involving a group of teenagers, but that's it. Nobody knew much of anything about this area. I was expecting much more than I got, but then again, has anyone been able to help me yet with the mystery of my new home?

I was disappointed, but it made me even more motivated to figure things out, so I embarked on my own research mission. I didn't have a library or anyone else left to turn to, so I looked to the internet. Too bad I didn't begin there. I found a lot of information. I also read a ton of books about the paranormal and learned that Stephanie was also a draw for paranormal activity because of her age. The fact that Stephanie was going through puberty made her energy more attractive and open to spirits.

I looked up contact information for one of the authors from one of the books I read. I couldn't believe I actually found a phone number for him. I doubted it was the right one, but tried it, anyway. I nervously dialed his number. He answered right on the third ring.

"Hello, Jefferson here, how can I help you?"

"I hope you don't mind that I called you. You don't know me, but I just read one of your books about the paranormal. I was wondering if I could ask you a few questions."

"Always happy to help a fan."

"I'm definitely a fan of yours, just not much of a fan of what's happening in my life right now."

"I understand. When the paranormal touches our lives, it's very hard coming to terms with it right away."

"I had a paranormal experience at a young age. It's the only experience I had until recently. I found out I could see multiple auras, but I hadn't seen another spirit since I was sixteen. It wasn't until we moved into our new home recently that everything started going crazy again."

"Mind telling me a little about your first paranormal experience?"

"I was relaxing in our living room one evening listening to music and saw a Civil War soldier standing across the room."

What he said next blew me away.

"For people who can see spirits it's very common for the first one to be a Civil War soldier. I've heard the same thing from many people I've talked to."

That's the same thing Theresa said to me.

"It also sounds like you might have a poltergeist."

"A what?"

"Poltergeist."

"I've been told that before."

"I suggest you take some time to research what a poltergeist is. It's a lot for me to explain in a short amount of time. Basically, it's created from a child going through puberty, and/or someone who has gone through trauma or abuse."

That explains a lot.

"I can tell you we have both. My daughter is entering puberty and my mother abused me as a child."

"My guess is, you're the one who created the poltergeist. Most likely you started creating it at a young age and that can make a poltergeist even more destructive. Poltergeists are created the same as humans are. They begin as children, move into teenagers, and finally adulthood. Adult poltergeists are very destructive, but they can be dealt with. It just takes time."

Wonderful.

I didn't like what I was hearing, but he was helpful and knowledgeable. He really helped me understand more about what I was dealing with. Well, at least one aspect of what I was dealing with. I didn't want to tell him everything; I'm especially not comfortable telling him I think we have a demon in our home. *Not yet, anyway.*

"One last thing I want to say to you before I go. Moving won't make the activity go away, it will most likely just follow you. Best to deal with it."

It really was the perfect storm.

"Stay safe and don't let those entities get the better of you. Remember, you have the power."

Easier said than done. I have power? Since when? I don't feel very powerful. If I were so powerful, then why can't I just shut this all down like I did when I was a teen?

The following day, Jefferson called me back with some additional information.

"I did some more research last night and was surprised to learn that there had been a Civil War battle fought right in the same area where you used to live. I could even pinpoint one of the battles on the same street you lived on when you saw the spirit of a Civil War soldier."

Amazing.

"Before they built houses, it was a thick forest area."

"Yes, some forest is still there. I used to explore it when I was in high school since it was just a block away."

I was completely blown away. I never would have known that if it hadn't been for him.

Well, I have now solved the mystery of my soldier. What about the Indians? I hope someday I can figure out why they are here. Meanwhile, I need to find someone who can help me clear this house.

Good thing I have another appointment with Theresa tomorrow. Maybe she can help me kick the poltergeist out of my house. In the meantime, I learned more about them since two people have told me they suspect poltergeists. It surprised me to learn that a poltergeist can lead to something even darker, as in a full demonic presence. I'm still struggling to wrap my head around the fact that a poltergeist is created by a living person who has, or is, undergoing some form of trauma. Chaotic and intense energy within a person can manifest in the form of psychic phenomena seen with these entities. A poltergeist can manifest in the form of knocks on walls or flooring, movement of objects, and has been known to throw things. The longer a poltergeist is around a person, the stronger it gets. I also found out it's even stronger when paranormal activity centers on a person who has psychic abilities that they don't completely understand.

It's amazing how perfectly this describes what I'm going through. Also, the fact that Stephanie was going through puberty only added to the creation of the perfect paranormal storm. The activity is mostly associated with a female child over a male because the female body produces a greater amount of energy during puberty. It was two-fold. Stephanie going through puberty and my abusive childhood most likely created a powerful poltergeist. I believe trauma and paranormal often go hand in hand. This isn't the best news for me, however. I might always have to deal with this, and I won't be able to move away from it. How do I free myself from it all? Will I have to live this nightmare for the rest of my life? I better get it together because there's no way I can go through life feeling this terrified all the time.

26

I'm relieved there's been less activity lately. Either that, or I'm becoming accustomed to it. Not that it couldn't change in a moment's time. It's the constant fear of the unknown I'm living with every single day. I'm excited to see Theresa today. I'm hoping she can help me clear the dark energy out of my home. The last thing I expected her to say was that I had the power to clear it myself.

"You're a very powerful medium. Didn't I already tell you that?"

"Yes, I'm just not sure I believe it."

"You have the abilities and the power to clear your home. You need to take your power back. I will tell you what to do."

"If you say so, I will try."

Still, I didn't believe what Theresa was telling me. How could I be so special? Yes, I can randomly see and hear spirits, but that was never by my own doing. It was just random, and I had absolutely no control over it. But, if Theresa feels so strongly that I can do this, I owe it to her and myself to give it a try.

Theresa told me because of my abilities it opened a portal to the other side to allow spirits or entities, good or bad, to pass through it. I've also learned that spirits seek me out because they honed in on my ability to sense the paranormal. This confirmed everything I've been feeling and validated to me I'm not crazy.

Theresa armed me with more supplies. She gave me white sage sticks, blessed salt and lavender oil. I know it's up to me and me alone to kick this evil out. I left feeling stronger and more capable.

When I returned home, I used the lavender oil Theresa gave me and made the sign of the cross above every door. It's used to clear negative energy, but it also helps calm my nerves. Something I'm in desperate need of these days. I sprinkled blessed salt in the four corners of the home as I've done before. I also spread it across every doorway. Salt is used to seal the house so no spirits can come inside. Sage has a vibration that dispels negativity and malevolent entities. I waited until I was alone to burn the sage. Sage is used to bless and cleanse.

It took about three days until the moment came when I was completely alone. I'm a terrible procrastinator, but I also felt like I needed this time to mentally prepare. I was still afraid, but even more determined it was going to work. Theresa also told me that intention was extremely important. I was to set an intention to get rid of everything in my house and be stern about it. Show the entities I meant business. I was determined to show the spirits who the actual owner of the house was. This time it was going to work, I could feel it. I felt deeply empowered like never before. I called upon my spirit guides and my warrior angel, Saint Michael. I feel reassured since I don't have to do this alone. I've called out to Saint Michael before, and I know he's saved me a few times already. I feel like we are warriors together in the fight. It's the feeling of taking a stand. Today was my stand. Let the battle begin.

I yelled at the top of my lungs.

"This is a house of God."

I gained more and more strength as I yelled. I put my hand up in the air and called out to Saint Michael, the strongest warrior in heaven.

Saint Michael, the Archangel,

defend us in battle.
Be our protection against the wickedness and snares of the devil;
May God rebuke him, we humbly pray;
And do thou, O Prince of the Heavenly Host,
by the power of God,
thrust into hell Satan and all evil spirits
who wander through the world for the ruin of souls. Amen.

I spread sage smoke all around in every corner of the house while repeatedly chanting this prayer. I let it all out. I stood there angry and victorious. My will was stronger, and I knew I was winning. I could feel it. My entire body was vibrating with energy as I tapped into my power. They were no match for me at this point. I felt a wind tunnel vacuum it all out. The energy in my home felt much lighter, and it was finally peaceful again. That night I slept better than I have in a very long time, undisturbed. It felt like heaven. Thank God for Theresa's guidance, my spirit guides, and of course Saint Michael. I'm finally free.

Now that the activity has calmed down, I can have a little fun in my life again. I have a new neighbor I've been dying to hang out with. They are a newlywed couple, Tracy and Owen. Prior to them, another neighbor who was renting moved out in only two weeks. I didn't even get to know who they were. I'd heard they made a lot of 911 calls prior to moving out for good. The first neighbors who lived next door was the family with the two cute little girls who moved out in the middle of the night. I sure would love to find out where they are. I'm dying to ask why they moved out the way they did. I suspect I know why, but asking that question is hard for me. I don't want to risk looking like a weirdo. We haven't even lived here an entire year and this is already our fourth neighbor.

I knocked on Tracy's door and she answered.

"Hello, I hope I'm not bothering you. I'm Julie, your next-door neighbor. I'm going on a little walk and was wondering if you'd like to join me."

"Thanks Julie, I'd love that, let me get my shoes on."

I waited on the front porch for her to come back out. I found it a little strange that she didn't invite me inside to wait for her. I need to stop being so suspicious. It means nothing, and it certainly doesn't mean she's hiding the fact that her house is also haunted. *Even though I had my suspicions.* I just want to make a new friend. I will not ask her about any activity in her house either. At least, not today.

"I found a new area I'd like to go back and explore, but I'm too chicken to go alone, so I'm glad you agreed to come with me."

"Are you talking about the cemetery in the middle of the next block?"

"Well yes, I am!"

"Great, let's go explore together."

Tracy seemed cool enough. I'm glad I went over and introduced myself.

"What do you make of the remnants of old houses in the area?"

"Not a clue. I tried to get some information at the local library and when that turned out to be a dead-end *pun intended,* I went next door to City Hall. Nobody had any information about when the homes were built, and there's no list of the names of the people buried in the cemetery. At the very least, I was hoping to find out if they assigned anybody to maintain it. It doesn't look like it's been cared for in a very long time. Can you believe neither the library nor the city acknowledged it's even there?"

"Yeah, that is surprising."

Tracy looked at me a little perplexed.

"Sounds like there's a story there."

"I tried to research our neighborhood. They didn't even have any information about who owned the rock crushing quarry that is now our lake. If my uncle hadn't worked there, I never would have known it existed."

"That is really odd."

"Tell me about it."

I'm feeling comfortable with Tracy, but still not enough to talk about what I really wanted to talk about. Besides, now that I've cleansed my home, there might not be anything to talk about. I just need to get my life back to normal and this is an impressive start. I deserve to have a paranormal free day.

"Hey Julie, come check this out. Did you notice this when you were here last?"

"No, I didn't, what is it?"

"No clue. I definitely want to find out though."

Tracy had ventured a short distance off to the right of the pathway. I ran over to where she was standing to find an unusually mounded-up area. Everything around it was flat. It didn't look like it had naturally formed, and it really stood out from the rest of the surroundings.

Tracy laughed when I asked her, "Want to go ask the city what this is?"

I love making people laugh.

We really had no clue what this mounded area was, but it wasn't naturally made, that we knew for sure. We walked around the cemetery and tried to read some of the headstones, but we could only make out a date on one of them. It was dated back to the year 1800.

"I bet that's why the city doesn't have any records on this cemetery. People didn't keep records back that far."

"That's a good point. Hey Julie, what about these abandoned old homes? Did you ask anyone about them?"

"No. Hey, maybe we could go to the library sometime and do some research. Between the two of us, maybe we can solve this mystery."

"Sure, but I must tell you, we won't be living here much longer."

"Oh?"

"We are building a new home. It surprised us when the owners agreed to rent to us for such a short time."

"Wow, that is surprising."

I wasn't surprised at all. The owners were having one hell of a time getting anyone to stay longer than a couple weeks in that place.

As we walked back toward our neighborhood, I asked her where they were moving to.

"We are building a house out in the country. It's about ten miles from here. There isn't a home within five miles of us and we can't wait. We are hoping to be self-sufficient and live off the land."

Yikes, I never want to live out in the country, and I can't imagine being so isolated. I never want to live off grid either. I like warm running water. I especially like having people living close by. To each their own, I guess.

When we got back to our homes, I thanked her for taking a walk with me and gave her my phone number in case she ever needed anything. We spoke a little more about making plans to go get coffee sometime, and then I said goodbye. I was dying to get back home to do some research on that mystery mound we just found in what I'm now calling my "enchanted forest." There's just something mystical about this place. It draws me in and makes me want to know more.

It didn't take long before I found a ton of information. What surprised me the most was how much it tied in with my Indian spirits. I knew there had to be a significant reason for seeing the Indian warriors. Maybe there's a connection between the warriors and this land. I remember wondering why I saw a Civil War soldier, but it took many more years until I understood why. There's an important significance to this, I can feel it in my bones.

This is very intriguing, but also quite sad. While researching, came across some information making me wonder if the mound we found is called an, "effigy mound." I never heard of an effigy mound before. An "effigy mound" is another name for "Indian burial ground." They usually built them in the shape of animals, but the one we saw didn't appear to be in the shape of any animal. As I did more research, I think I discovered why. I didn't even know if any Indians ever lived in this area. I assumed so, but I never really gave it much thought. My research was astounding.

Recent documents have been discovered that address the Kalapuya mounds in the Tualatin and Yamhill valleys. The most famous Kalapuya Indians were along the Calapooia River and tributaries between Corvallis and Sweet Home. Years ago, they discovered over 100 effigy mounds that used to exist. An effigy mound is described as "a raised pile of earth built in the shape of an animal, symbol, human, or other figure and contains one or more human burials."

The city I live in is in Oregon along the Willamette River at a former site of a Calapooia Indian village. The site was "rediscovered" by a Methodist missionary group led by Jason Lee. They made their way along the Oregon Trail originating from England. *This is remarkable.*

live in the same valley as the Indians lived long before me. When early white settlers arrived in the mid-1800s, they plowed over the ancient burial mounds to grow their crops and any remains inside were ground into the dirt. Hundreds of mounds were desecrated and completely wiped away. It's the same or possibly even worse than desecrating a cemetery. This is sacred Indian land that the early settlers completely disregarded and destroyed. Disrupting a grave like this is unbelievably disrespectful.

I'm not sure yet if the mounded-up area we found is in fact an effigy mound. It didn't seem to fit into the area. It was also close to the deserted cemetery we found. If this turns out to be an Indian burial mound, I believe it could have disrupted a lot of spiritual energy. This might be the cause for all the paranormal activity I've been experiencing lately. Maybe this is why I'm seeing Indian warriors. Is our neighborhood built on Indian land or worse, sacred Indian burial grounds? I believe it's all tied in somehow, but until I do more research, it's going to remain a mystery. I'm determined to learn more. I'm not sure why, but I sense I'm here for a reason and that reason just might be to find answers to these questions.

I'm on a mission.

It didn't take long for my research to uncover some very intriguing information. It felt like the more I learned, the more I craved. It became an obsession. I've lived in this area my entire life and this is the very first I've ever heard about effigy mounds. It surprised me to discover they built effigy mounds along the Willamette River. I live mere minutes from the Willamette. This is unreal. It felt like a big coincidence, but I don't really believe in coincidences. This was coming together as one big message for me and an even bigger mystery I was called upon to help put to rest. A tragedy that took place over 150 years ago leading to eternal unrest.

I think it's time for another walk. Stephanie has a friend whose family lives right on the river. Maybe her mother would like to go do a little exploration in her backyard with me. I decided to give her a call.

"Mary, this is Julie, Stephanie's mom. I have a question I'd like to ask you, maybe even a little favor."

"Sure, Julie what's up?"

"I was wondering if I could use your backyard for access to the Willamette River. I want to go exploring back there and I was wondering if you'd be interested in exploring with me."

"Why yes, I've always thought it would be fun to check out what's lurking behind me, I just haven't taken the time to do it yet."

"Let's go today, are you available now?"

"No time like the present, I always say. I don't have to pick Jaime up from school for a couple hours, so yes, now would be great."

"I'm on my way."

I didn't quite know how to tell her I was looking for Indian burial mounds. I'm not sure if she'd be too keen on that. I definitely don't know Mary well enough to tell her what's going on with my home, at least not yet. It's so hard to know who you can trust. I don't want to risk losing her before I had time to get to know her. She would think I'm the biggest freak show if she knew.

I probably should have walked to Mary's house, but I was too excited to get exploring and I didn't want to waste any time. I only have a couple hours, so better make the most of it. Mary's house is gorgeous. It's an enormous mansion in a very upscale neighborhood. Way nicer than ours. I wonder if weird stuff goes on here too, but I'll just keep that to myself for now.

I parked my car on her gorgeous cobblestone driveway and walked up to her front door. Mary opened the door before I could ring the doorbell.

"Hi Mary, are you ready for our little adventure?"

"Absolutely."

"What are you looking for primarily?"

I almost choked when she asked me that question. I'm a terrible liar so I just blurted it out.

"Have you ever heard of an Indian effigy mound?"

"Yes, and I've also heard they were built in our area."

"As a matter of fact, I think I already found a small one in the forest across the street from our neighborhood. Did you know there's an old abandoned cemetery inside there as well?"

"Seriously? You're joking."

"Nope, not at all. I even found some headstones that are dated back to the 1800's. Most of them are illegible, but the one I was able to read was dated 1840."

"That's amazing, Julie. You are quite the explorer."

"Not really, just looking for answers."

"What type of answers?"

"Well Mary, if I tell you I can't un-tell you. But for some strange reason I feel very comfortable being honest with you, even though we don't know each other that well yet. Every time I've been around you, there's just something about you that makes me feel safe."

"Well, maybe that's because I'm an Empath, too."

Mary blew me away when she said that.

"How did you know I'm an Empath?"

"Well, I'm being told you are, am I right?"

"Who told you? I haven't told anyone, not even my husband."

"Don't freak out, Ok?"

"Ok."

"Your spirit guides told me."

Amazing . . .

"I just started seeing spirits again. I've been trying to handle it better this time and not freak out like I did years ago. I have someone, a counselor I just started seeing, and she's great at helping me deal with it all."

"Julie, there's no reason to be afraid. Some of us just have gifts that other people don't have. It doesn't mean we are bad people. It's easy for me to recognize when someone else is gifted. Just be patient. In time you will come to appreciate your gifts."

"Thanks Mary, I'm still struggling with accepting it as a gift."

"Took me a while, too. Now tell me, why are you looking for this effigy mound? I know where one is. Would you like me to take you to it?"

"That would be awesome."

"Are you seeing Indians? Or have you gotten any messages from them? They used to be very prominent in our area."

"I've been dreaming about a couple of Indian warriors who claim to be watching over me. They told me I have two portals in my hall closet. One portal is to the spiritual world, the other is a portal to hell."

"That sounds terrifying. Have you had any activity that makes you fearful there's something demonic in your home?"

"Where do I start?"

"Julie, I feel I need to share something with you. I'm a shaman and I have a close friend who's a Reiki master. If you ever need any help cleansing your home, you can call on us and we will be there to help. You don't have to be alone with this anymore."

"Mary, thank God I called you today. I never knew you were this spiritual."

"Julie, I believe something led you to me today."

"I couldn't agree more."

Mary guided me to the most amazing effigy mound. They made it in the shape of a bird. Mary knew so much about them. She said that most of the mounds were formed in the shape of birds and bears. They also made them in the shape of bison, lynx, panthers, turtles, and water spirits.

"Mary, I read where the settlers came through here and destroyed most of the effigy mounds to plant their crops."

"Yes, it's a tragic part of history. What the settlers did to the Indians is terribly disrespectful."

"Julie, I believe your Indian spirits are here to protect you. I just tried to tap into the energy in your home and that's the vibe I'm getting. I also feel something very negative is in your home that I need to warn you about. Be careful. I'm here for you if you ever need any help."

Mary had to head back home. I sat down on a rock near the effigy mound with tears streaming down my face. It was the same feeling I had when I walked into the metaphysical store. It felt so cleansing and I just let myself go. I cried and cried until I couldn't cry anymore. It was a moment of pure healing and acceptance. It was so comforting to finally find someone I could talk to without risking ridicule. I also believed Mary was sent to me by angels. I don't know what else it could have been. I think sometimes we are guided in the direction we need to go. It certainly was true for me. Today signified the beginning of the next chapter of my incredible journey.

27

Over the last few weeks Mary and I had become close friends, and I grew to trust her. I felt comfortable sharing most of the paranormal events that had taken place in my home. My stories fascinated her. She was especially interested in whatever was mimicking our voices. She had an incredible theory about it.

"I believe you saw each other's doppelgangers."

"We didn't actually see them, though. We only heard something mimic our voices . . . perfectly mimicked our voices in the most terrifying way."

"Just because you didn't see it doesn't mean it's not there. I'm relieved you didn't see them."

"Mary, what's a doppelganger? I've never heard that word before."

"A doppelganger is a German word meaning 'double walker.' According to legend, a doppelganger is a supernatural creature that is a duplicate of a living human being. Even Abraham Lincoln saw his doppelganger in a mirror before his death. It's believed that if you see your own doppelganger, it's an omen of death. Because you only heard each other's voices it's most likely just a warning about something, or it could mean you're in for some bad luck."

"Wow, well at least it's not an omen of death. I'm impressed with how much you know about the spiritual world."

"Honey, I have a lot more experience than you and I've learned to accept my gifts. You were too afraid of anyone finding out about your abilities, *which is understandable,* and shut them down. It was just a matter of time before they came back to you. Too bad it all came flooding back at the same time, and now you're feeling the full impact."

"How do I learn to not be so afraid?"

"I think that will come with time. The spiritual world isn't all bad. Sometimes spirits are here to help us. I believe you have lots of work to do before you can fully accept your abilities as a gift. You couldn't be in a better place to practice. This area is highly active."

I couldn't agree more. This area is crazy active.

"Everything scares me, but I also believe I have some spirits with me who are trying to guide me."

"Yes, you definitely do. You're a very powerful medium. You've just learned how to perfect avoidance."

"I'm a powerful medium?"

"You will see, you will learn, and eventually you will accept. Once that happens, your abilities will open up and you'll do great things with them."

One thing's for sure, Mary couldn't have been more right about the warning. It had only been a couple days since we spoke when all hell broke loose in our home. But this time, is wasn't of a paranormal nature.

Jeff was on the computer paying bills.

"Julie, our gas and water bill are extremely high this month. It's over double what it was last month. Do you have any idea why that is?"

"Not at all, nothing's changed that I know of."

"I'm going to call a heating professional to come take a look."

The following morning a heating and cooling contractor came to our house. He checked our water heater and gas furnace, and everything looked fine. Then, he crawled under the house and found a major flood in the crawlspace. We were completely oblivious. We hadn't even noticed that the flood had warped some of the floor boards in the kitchen.

"Ma'am have you noticed how warm the kitchen floor feels? It shouldn't be this warm in the middle of November."

I felt so stupid, but I had so many other things on my mind I really hadn't noticed.

"What do we do now?"

"This is going to need extensive repair. I know of at least two pipes that are broken. Unfortunately, one of the broken pipes leads to your water heater. That's the reason your water and gas bill are so high. The water is scalding under your house."

"Any idea what this could cost?"

"I won't have an exact estimate until we look further, but I would guess it's not going to be cheap."

"Good Lord, I think we need to call our insurance company."

"Good luck, most insurance companies won't cover floods."

I called Jeff and gave him the good news.

"Jeff, can you please call our insurance agent and ask him to come over . . . like ASAP?"

"Yes, I'm heading home now. I'm actually not too far from his office. I will stop by and see if he's available."

Luckily, our insurance agent was still in his office and had time to come over. Unfortunately, it was Friday afternoon and nothing was going to get done until Monday. The insurance guy was very nice and everything, but he didn't have much hope for us. What are we going to do if this isn't covered? *I'm panicking.* We don't have that kind of money.

"Guys, I won't know until Monday if you're covered or not. I'm going to do my best for you, but I don't want you to get your hopes up."

Waiting until Monday was agony. Two days of pure stress. We had no clue how we were going to afford any of this. At least nothing happened in the paranormal realm to add to my anxiety over the weekend. I think all the entities knew I needed a break. At 8:00 a.m. on Monday morning we got the phone call. Jeff answered his phone and put it on speaker when he saw it was from Casey.

"I have great news for you. The builder of your home used CPVC pipes throughout the house. The builder didn't know he was using defective pipes, but these have an inherent defect that made them fail sooner than they should have. These pipes were recalled shortly after they built your home."

After hearing this glorious news, I couldn't help myself. I started bawling my eyes out. I didn't even care who knew it.

"Casey, I don't even know what to say other than thank you. It's been an incredibly tough weekend."

"I can imagine. I'm coming out this morning to talk more with you guys. With the coverage of the repairs also comes coverage for your family to move out and stay in a hotel. We have determined it's not safe for you to stay in your home. I will explain more when I get there."

Jeff and I looked at each other in complete disbelief. We couldn't believe what just happened. We were both relieved and a little frightened. What did Casey mean it wasn't safe to stay in our home? I know there's a flood under the house, but how is that dangerous? All they need to do is clear out the flood and fix the pipes. I can't wait to talk to Casey. It felt like it took forever for him to arrive when it had only been a little over an hour. Casey brought a couple people with him. These people were experts in the field of something we never heard of before.

"This is Mark and Frank. They are experts in radon abatement. Our instruments found a large amount of radon under your house, therefore rendering it uninhabitable."

"What's radon?"

"Radon is a dangerous radioactive gas that comes from contaminated groundwater. The flooding under your house has caused a breakdown of uranium in the soil, rock and water, and that's how it gets into the air you breathe. We have determined your house had twenty-five times the normal amount of radon, and that's not healthy. We want you to find a hotel to stay at while we do repairs. Your insurance will cover the costs."

Thank the Lord for defective pipes, otherwise this repair would have devastated us financially. I'm eternally grateful to everyone for doing the investigating it took to find the root cause of our problem.

However, it's close to Thanksgiving and I have to go find a hotel. That's not going to be easy. To my surprise, the only hotel that had anything available was the beautiful upscale hotel downtown. This was also the most expensive and newest hotel in town. I was certain the insurance company wouldn't want to pay for this. All I can do is call Casey and ask.

"Casey, I've got a minor problem. All the hotels in our town are full, and the only one I could find is also the most expensive hotel in town."

"Yeah, I was afraid of that being so close to Thanksgiving. How much is the hotel?"

I was almost afraid to say.

"$260 per night."

"I will approve the hotel for now. We might have to ask you to move to another one after Thanksgiving. We've assigned Greg to be your adjuster. He's the one who will help you with expenses. We cover the cost of meals, too. Expect a call from Greg sometime this afternoon to advise you on how to turn in receipts, etc."

Wow, I hadn't even thought about food yet. We went from being terrified we'd have to go broke, to being approved by the insurance company and having everything covered. Jeff gets bonus points for buying the best coverage money can buy. What a relief.

Everything was so great, and we were even a little excited to stay in a swanky hotel for a while. *Well, at first.* It's kind of like how excited you are for the first winter snow. It's beautiful and fun for a while, but when the snow doesn't let up for weeks . . . you're begging for it to stop. That's exactly how this felt.

I had to go home frequently to pick up additional items. I couldn't stay in the house long enough to do laundry, so I also got to go spend time in a laundromat. We had a kitchenette in the room so that saved on eating out all the time. Eating out in restaurants gets old real fast. We also had a small refrigerator and a microwave.

One day I was home picking up some additional clothing. Inside our walk-in closet is a hatch that led to the crawl space under the house. I was standing inside the closet when a man came up through the floor. We were both startled when we came face to face. He didn't speak any English, so he just nodded his head and said, "Ola." I said "Ola" back and abruptly left. I remember feeling sorry for the guys who had to suit up and crawl around under our house to fix the pipes. I hope it paid them well.

Maybe I really am an Empath.

They brought in huge scrubbing machines to clean the air in our home. These ran constantly, day and night. All the workers wore face masks whenever they were inside our house. I didn't have one, so I tried to get in and out quickly. The kitchen floor had to be replaced as well as the floors in the bathrooms and the laundry room. I often wondered if anything paranormal ever happened to any of the workers while they were at our house. Nobody ever complained or mentioned it, so I kept my secrets to myself. The only thing we had to pay for was mold remediation. They examined our attic and found the flood under our house had caused mold to grow in the attic. That cost was around $2,500, but we gladly paid it. We were so grateful we didn't have to pay for everything. I was surprised to hear that mold had grown into the attic.

We ended up staying in our lovely hotel through Christmas and a couple months after that. I was so sick of that place by the time they cleared us to go back home. I could write a book on what it's like to live in a hotel. *Not my cup of tea.* Friday and Saturday nights were the worst. Because of it being the holidays, partiers were coming and going at all hours of the night. None of us were sleeping very well, which made for a lot of frayed nerves. If you ever have to live in a hotel, get the room furthest away from the elevator. We weren't so fortunate.

Looking back, I believe the doppelgangers were there to warn us. We had a flooding issue under the house that was creating deadly radon gas, and we didn't even know it. There are many theories about why doppelgangers exist. In our case, I'd like to think they were actually there to save us. We haven't heard or seen them since.

28

T he day they gave us clearance to move back into our home couldn't come soon enough. I will never forget the phone call I received from the insurance adjuster.

"Julie, are you ready to get out of your luxury hotel and move back home?"

"Am I! Please tell me you're not joking this time."

Our insurance adjuster was a nice guy who fancied himself a comedian. I was desperate to go home. Sounds funny now that I think about it since I was free from paranormal activity the entire time we were in the hotel. I'm not sure why because I've heard hotels are notoriously haunted. I have no explanation, but it was a pleasant break. But now, I'm beyond ready to go back home.

I packed in a matter of minutes. Jeff left work to come help me carry everything out to the car. That was no easy feat. Our room was on the fifth floor. Once we got to the first-floor lobby, we had to walk down a long hallway to another elevator that took us down to a parking garage. From there it was another hike to the car. Our hotel was huge.

The night before they sent us home was pretty exciting. At 3:00 a.m. I woke to the sound of a really loud and annoying alarm. Once I was fully awake, I realized it was a fire alarm. I woke Jeff and Stephanie up, *reminded Jeff to put on pants,* grabbed my purse with my car keys and we ran out the door. On our way out of our hotel room, I saw a man across the hall desperately trying to get back inside his room with his key card.

"Dude! Do you hear the fire alarm? I'm sure the hotel has automatically locked you out of your room. Please come with us to look for the stairs."

"I need to get inside my room! I have an important meeting I have to get to and I need my briefcase."

It angered me he had such little concern for his own safety.

"Well, you're not getting through that door until the hotel releases it. Come with us to search for a way out of here. I'm sure people at your meeting will understand."

What was wrong with this guy? It seemed odd to me all he cared about was getting his briefcase and making it to his precious meeting. It was such an inconvenience for him having to leave the hotel, even if it meant saving his own life. He was growing angrier by the second, and I worried he was going to try to break the door down. When he started swearing, I stopped him and pointed to my child. Have some respect, buddy.

What really surprised me were the amount of people standing around waiting for the elevator. I reminded them that taking an elevator when a fire alarm is going off was a bad idea, and asked them to help us look for the stairs. We found an emergency exit at the end of the hallway and walked down the stairs to the lobby. I couldn't smell any smoke, so that was a relief. There were lots of people hanging out in the lobby when we got there. Five minutes later, the fire department came and escorted us all outside. We walked down to the parking garage, got in our car and left. On our way out, the sprinklers were activated inside the parking garage. At least they didn't come on until after we were inside the car. It was like driving through a waterfall when we exited the garage. Later, we found out it was just a false alarm. I was really intrigued by how some other hotel guests behaved and that they didn't know the proper procedure for a hotel fire. I wasn't sure either, but I knew better than to get on an elevator. I can't imagine getting stuck in an elevator in the middle of an actual fire. That would be horrifying.

Home sweet home. It actually felt like the first day we moved in all over again. We had brand-new wood floors in the kitchen. The bathroom floors all had to be retiled, and the laundry room floor had to be replaced. Most of the carpet had to be ripped out and replaced as well. Before we came back home, we had a radon and carbon monoxide detector installed. I'm not taking any chances. I never even heard of radon before this happened to us. The scary part is, it could happen again. The insurance company would not pay to replace all the defective pipes, they would only pay to replace them if they broke. I kind of feel like we're living on top of a time bomb. It could go off again at any moment. I just hope it gives me some time to forget what it's like to live in a hotel first.

If that's even possible.

It's so nice to be back home again. It was weird spending Christmas in a hotel. One Christmas I spent in the hospital. I guess between the two I'd much rather be in a hotel. It gave me a newfound respect for people who have to travel a lot for work. That kind of lifestyle isn't for me. I guess it's all in what you get used to, but I never adjusted to living in a hotel.

The day after we moved back home, a moving van pulled up in front of the house next door. It looks like today is moving day for Tracy and Owen. I walked outside and stood in our driveway. I saw Tracy come out of her house, so I walked over to talk to her. Maybe now is my chance to ask a neighbor if they've ever experienced anything paranormal in their home like I have. Until now, I've been too chicken.

"Hey Tracy, are you guys moving out to the country today?"

"Yes, I can hardly wait. Did you know the Yang's from a couple doors down moved while you were gone?"

"No, I didn't know that. I didn't really know them. They had a cute little beagle. I only talked to their boys a couple times when they were walking their dog. The wife always seemed on edge whenever I saw her. She even jumped once when I walked up behind her at the grocery store. I didn't mean to frighten her. I tried to keep my distance whenever I saw her after that."

"Julie, you're too funny. Don't blame yourself, she was just a jumpy lady."

"Tracy, you're terrible. I'm really going to miss you."

"I might miss you, not this house, but I will miss you."

"Tracy, speaking of the house . . ."

I figured they were already moving, so why not ask? I finally feel brave enough to ask her if they ever experienced any unusual activity in their home. It's so hard for me to ask this question, so I'm going to leave the word "paranormal" out. Since they were on their way out, I wanted to know if strange activity was the reason. I found her answer to be quite odd.

"Have you or Owen ever experienced any unusual activity in your home during the time you lived here?"

"No, we've never experienced anything weird, and we always had positive energy in our home."

She seemed a little nervous talking about it. I thought I could hear a bit of quivering in her voice. Might have just been my imagination, but I don't think so. I can read body language pretty well and she was definitely feeling uncomfortable. That I was sure about. Tracy went on to say . . .

"Many people have even commented on how inviting and positive the energy is."

Well, that was weird. Maybe it's just me, but I found it to be an incredibly strange answer. In any home I've ever lived in, not one single person has ever commented on the "energy." I mean, is that a normal thing to say?

Tracy and Owen lasted longer than any other family who previously lived there, almost an entire five months. They never came back to visit, either. I called Tracy many times to invite them over. We had a neighborhood get together and a few of the neighbors asked them to come to it. Tracy always made up some lame excuse why they were too busy. They never came back, and they never invited us to their new home. It seemed as if they wanted a clean break from the neighborhood. Yeah, you have nothing but positive energy in your home.

Sure thing.

So far, so good on the paranormal front. I was a little concerned when we moved back home. Mary warned me that any change made to a home can increase activity. For example, if a house is remodeled and the spirits don't approve, things can get ugly. Our house was still considered new, and it wasn't remodeled by any means, but there was some construction work done out of necessity.

I was loving the peace and quiet.

It was Friday and Jeff took the afternoon off. When he got home, he asked me if I'd like to go for a ride out in the country. I love taking long drives on country roads and just getting lost. It's fun to find little hole in the wall restaurants to eat at. Mostly, I just love exploring new places. I jumped at the chance to get away for a drive. Stephanie was spending the weekend at her dad's, so off we went.

We had just pulled out of the driveway when Jeff came up with a fun new idea.

"Have you ever been to Zena?"

"Never heard of Zena, what is it? Is it a town?"

"Yes, it's a tiny community on the way to McMinnville. I'm surprised you've never heard of it since your aunt lives in McMinnville. Well, I'd like to take you there and show you the little white church on the hill. Since you've never been there, you're going to love it."

"Not that I don't appreciate the effort, but why would I want to go look at a church?"

"Because it looks like it came straight out of *Little House on the Prairie* and it has a cemetery next to it."

"Oh, hell yeah, let's go!"

I used to be a big fan of *Little House*. I used to get up and watch it every morning before work.

It was a lovely drive out in the country with beautiful hills and valleys and fun winding roads. The sun was peeking through the trees and we had the road all to ourselves. *It was perfect.* When we arrived at the bottom of the long driveway up to the church, I couldn't believe what I was looking at. It looked exactly how Jeff had described it. The church was white with a steeple on top and windows so old they were wavy. It was awesome. I felt like I had just stepped back in time. The cemetery was on the left side of the church situated on a beautiful hillside. Jeff parked along the side of the church and we got out of the car.

As soon as I stepped out of the car, I heard heavy footsteps on the gravel road that surrounded the church. It sounded like it was coming from around the left side of the church. We couldn't see anyone because we parked on the right side of the church. I know Jeff heard it too because we both paused and stood there dead still. It got eerily quiet while we stood there waiting for someone to come walking around the corner or something else to happen. We couldn't even hear any birds chirping.

"Jeff, did you hear that?"

"Yes, it's probably just a caretaker or something. We will just act like we belong here and there shouldn't be any issues."

Jeff and I stood there and waited for the caretaker to walk toward us, but nobody came. We continued hearing heavy footsteps that sounded like they were making their way closer to us, but we never saw one single person. After a while, Jeff gave me a look of complete disbelief. He even looked a little pale.

"Kinda weird when you can't explain it, isn't it?"

"I'm sure they just ducked inside a door and they're in the church right now watching us."

"Well, in that case, you'd better watch your step."

Jeff is a total skeptic and I'm sure he will always be a skeptic. It annoys me sometimes how much of a skeptic he is, but it's genuinely who he is. Nothing I can say or do about it. He'll never change. In Jeff's defense, I'm sure I can be pretty annoying, too.

Jeff and I gave up on finding anyone, so we walked around the church and look inside through the windows. The church was quaint and looked very old. They actually still hold Sunday morning services here. I always say I'd like to go to one someday, but I still haven't gotten around to doing so. We walked around the cemetery reading some names and dates on the headstones. At least this was a properly cared for cemetery, much better than the one inside the forest near our home. I remember thinking maybe I will go over and give it a little love and clean it up a bit. It's just so eerie. I felt uncomfortable both times when I was there. Zena cemetery is the opposite. Very calm and relaxing. I had a sneaky feeling the footsteps we heard on the gravel wasn't from a live person. I believe it was a cemetery guardian making sure we weren't up to no good. They had some problems with vandalism in the past. I don't get how anyone could be so disrespectful. These headstones dated back to the early 1800's. They are irreplaceable, yet some people just don't care. We were walking toward our car when we heard the footsteps again. They were coming up from behind us this time, each footstep sounding louder on the gravel as we moved closer to our car.

The weird part, this time I wasn't afraid at all. I had a sense that it was just a caretaker watching over the cemetery. We saw nothing and as soon as we reached our car, it stopped. Jeff guessed it was about ten feet away from us when it stopped walking. Jeff was way more scared than I was. He had to act stoic and hide it, but I knew. He'd never admit to anything scaring him, especially not something he couldn't see. He'd never give me the satisfaction of ever believing in anything paranormal . . . which completely sucks. This is my life day in and day out. How can he not believe? That's the part I just don't get. It's also the basis for many an argument.

"Hey Jeff, thanks for bringing me here, I love this place. It's so peaceful here. Also, thanks for showing me where some of your friends are buried. It's so tragic how they died. I didn't know you knew so many people who died in high school. Gone too soon."

"You've known a lot more. I never met anyone who knew so many people who died in such tragic ways."

He was right. I knew six kids from grade school alone who committed suicide. *All boys.* I knew many from high school who died in car accidents, two who died from a shooting in a bar and a couple who died from cancer. It is really strange when I think about it. Sometimes I feel like I have one foot in this world, and another in the afterlife.

"Hey Jeff, want to go see where some of my people are buried? We can just make a day of it touring cemeteries."

"Girl, you really know how to live."

"Pun intended?"

"Always."

I also wanted to show Jeff where some of my family members are buried. Some of them had silly names. Grandma Eva is buried close to where I used to live as a kid. I was only six when she died. I frequently rode my bike to visit her grave. I used to sit there for hours talking to her about my life. Now I realize I didn't have to sit next to where she's buried to talk to her. There was just something about being that close to her that comforted me. I needed that as a kid, too. My childhood was so stressful. My grandma was special and really made me feel loved.

"First stop is to visit Grandma Eva. I have a few friends buried there, too. My friend Maria, the one who died on duty as a police officer, is there. My other friend Pat isn't too far from Maria. He died in a tragic car crash shortly after graduation. In the mausoleum are a couple who died together in another car accident. Their parents buried them next to one another."

"Ok, wow . . . you really know lots of people who have died."

"Well, I'm sure there's more I'm not remembering. I also knew many people because my family has lived here for so many years. I'm the fifth generation who still lives in this town."

Our first stop was Belcrest Memorial cemetery. This is where my grandma's buried. It was my favorite cemetery in town. Most times when I visited, I'd get to see at least one deer, sometimes two. When my friend Pat was interred here, a group of us were hanging around reminiscing when suddenly, a mother and baby deer came running across the field mere feet from where we were standing. It was so beautiful it took our breaths away. We always considered it a gift from our friend and his way of saying goodbye.

We left Belcrest and drove to the Catholic cemetery where a lot of my fathers' family is buried. My father had a great grandfather with the funniest last name, "Herman Hemann" was his name. We called him, "Herman the German." I wish I had known him before he died. Anyone with a name like that has got to have a sense of humor.

The last cemetery on our tour was, "Pioneer Cemetery." This is the oldest cemetery in town, with headstones dating back to the early 1800's. Some of the most prominent citizens in the city are buried here. The Bush family has a rather large ornate plot here. Part owner of Ladd & Bush bank, Asahel Bush also was a key figure during Oregon's formative years. His house is now a museum and the park next to it is called, "Bush's Pasture Park." It's a very well maintained gorgeous old park with a lovely rose garden.

While Jeff and I stood there admiring the Bush family plot, something a little further down the hill caught my eye. I was drawn to it for reasons I still don't fully understand. Jeff wandered off in a different direction as I walked through the cemetery toward the main road. Pioneer Cemetery used to be out in the country, but now it's on a major thoroughfare which cuts right through the middle of town. It was mid-April and unusually warm for this time of year. That alone made this experience even more perplexing. As I ventured closer to the main road there appeared to be a person looking down at a headstone. The strangest part was, whoever was standing there was wearing a full-length heavy wool coat with a larger than normal hood. The hood was pulled over their head. I couldn't get close enough to see a face, so I couldn't tell if this was a man or a woman. I found the heavy wool coat to be creepy and strange. It reminded me of something I saw when we took field trips to Mount Angel Abbey when I was a kid. The monks dressed exactly like this and always kept the hoods up over their heads. They would walk by us with their heads down, eyes turned toward the floor. For me, it made them appear even more intimidating. I thought they were trying to scare us kids on purpose. They never once spoke to any of us, either. It was just so creepy. I hated visiting the Abby. I never felt comfortable there, and none of us felt welcome. My anxiety level escalated the moment the bus pulled into the long, narrow driveway leading up to an ancient gothic-style building. I get anxious just thinking about it. Nothing about Catholic school was fun.

As I looked at this, whatever this was, I grew more and more intrigued by it. I wanted to stop moving closer to it, but I just couldn't help myself. I got within about twenty feet of it when something strange happened. It turned very slowly toward me, as if to face me, but kept its head down. How could it know I was there when it wasn't even looking at me or in my direction? It's like it instinctively knew I was approaching. I don't know what to call it other than "it." I stood frozen in place, yet I couldn't take my eyes off of it. I desperately wanted to turn and run away, but I couldn't. I wanted to scream for help, but no sound would come out. I tried to move my head to look back to see where Jeff was, but I was literally frozen in place. At that moment, I realized I was being controlled by this thing, then it started to slowly raise its head. *Slowly, very slowly.* It terrified me. I was soaking wet with sweat. I just stood there transfixed, staring at this thing. It's all I could do. It completely had me in its grip and was disabling my ability to move.

When it finally raised its head all the way up, I wasn't at all prepared for what I saw. This thing had no face. I was staring into a void of pure blackness. It looked like shiny black tape wrapped into an enormous ball that was moving and undulating in circles inside the heavy wool hood. When I saw something fly out from its hood that looked like a bolt of lightning, I broke free from its spell and took off running. I ran so fast that by the time I made it to Jeff, I was completely out of breath. All I could do was motion to him to get in the car. I jumped in the car, put the key in the ignition and got the hell out of there. I was parked on a dirt road inside the cemetery. I'm surprised I didn't knock over any headstones as I frantically drove away. All I could see behind me was a cloud of dust. I could have knocked something over and not even known it, that's how terrified I was.

I desperately wanted to figure out what this thing was, so I made another appointment with Theresa. I thought she might know what happened, and she did. She was so cool about it, too. She just calmly listened to my story like it was no big deal. When I finished talking, Theresa nonchalantly responded, "cemetery guardian."

"Theresa, first how do you always stay so calm and . . . what the heck is a cemetery guardian?"

"Well, they are there to guard the cemetery. I'm impressed you even saw one. I think that's super cool. You're even more gifted than I thought. I don't know of anyone who's ever interacted with a cemetery guardian before. They aren't there for people to see, and it's incredibly rare for anyone to actually come as close to one as you did. I've heard they're not supposed to interact with humans. That's pretty exciting, I wish I had been there to see it with you."

"Oh yeah, jolly good time it was. Theresa, I was scared out of my mind. I didn't think it was cool at all. It had me in some kind of weird hold too, I couldn't move an inch."

"That was probably just sheer terror on your part. I've never heard of a guardian having that kind of hold over anyone, but then again, anything is possible."

"How come this stuff doesn't scare you? Everything scares me."

"That's just because you're not used to it yet. You think every spirit is out to get you or it's a demon. Plus, didn't you talk to some paranormal investigators who put that fear into you?"

"Um, yeah, but how did you know that?"

"Well, I'm in contact with your spirit guides and they just told me."

Simply amazing . . .

Theresa never failed to impress. She was so incredibly gifted. I could only dream of being as amazing as her someday. She told me I was as gifted as her, even more so, but I was still too afraid. She also told me I have attention deficit disorder. That made it harder to quiet my mind, therefore making it tougher for entities to reach me.

"I have another message for you. It's about your spirit guides. I know who one of them is. Would you like to know, too?"

"Alright . . ."

"His name is Aredon, and he is very ancient and powerful. I'm told he's been with you your entire life. He has been assigned to your family throughout many past lives. You needed him to help guide you through your childhood. He's saved you many times. You really had more brushes with death than you realize. Aredon has been the one keeping you alive. He also rides along the outside of your car when you're driving."

"Incredible. I'm at a complete loss for words. I always sensed I had extra help. There was that time I was driving home through some mountains, and I swear my car went off the edge of a cliff. I would have surely died if it had. Suddenly, my car was just sitting still in the middle of the road, and I have no explanation for it."

"Yep, that was Aredon. He said there have been other instances when he's helped you on the road. He said you daydream too much when you're driving."

Makes sense, I know I'm a daydreamer. I also felt my car rise up and placed back onto the road in the middle of a tight curve. I can't wrap my head around it, but I truly believe it happened.

"Theresa, I just remembered another incident. I had just turned onto a steep driveway on my way to a friend's apartment, which was located at the top of the hill. It was dark that night and snowing a little. I hit a patch of ice and my car slid into the ditch on the opposite side of the road. I got out of my car and literally pushed it out of the ditch. To this day, I have no clue how I did that. I figured I had somehow tapped into some adrenaline that gave me superhuman strength. Or, was it Aredon?"

"Yes, Aredon just confirmed he helped you. Julie, he's always there with you."

Knowing this gave me a lot of peace, but I'm still finding it odd to think a spirit guide has the ability to hold on to the outside of my car. He must be huge and powerful. I just don't think my rational brain can really comprehend everything there is to know. Especially not Aredon, although I'm very grateful to have a powerful and ancient spirit guide. For some weird reason, it makes me feel special. Few things in my life have made me feel anywhere close to special. After hearing what Theresa had to say, I believe I needed the extra help as a child. Especially when dealing with my narcissistic, mentally ill mother. She really terrorized my life. I'm deeply grateful to Aredon and any other spirit guides who were, *and still are*, there to help me navigate through my crazy, mixed-up life.

Theresa has quite an interesting story about how she came into her own abilities. Theresa was diagnosed with a life-threatening illness. She told me, "My abilities were birthed out of severe trauma."

As the story goes, one day Theresa was standing in line at a Subway restaurant. She kept getting prodded by a spirit asking her to give a message to the man standing in line ahead of her.

"It was like I was standing there having an argument with someone I couldn't see. I knew it was a woman speaking to me and she was relentless."

"What was she saying to you?"

"She wanted me to tell the man in line ahead of me it was ok to eat at home."

"That's a strange request."

"She kept persisting until I gave in and tapped the gentleman on the shoulder. I told him I had an odd request to give him a message. When I said it was alright to eat at home, he broke down and cried. It took a while for him to compose himself again, but when he finally spoke, it blew me away. He told me his wife had died a couple months ago. Ever since she passed, he hadn't felt comfortable eating at home anymore."

"That's odd, I wonder why."

"He said it was because his wife always cooked and they sat together at the kitchen table and ate together. He just couldn't bring himself to sit alone at the table anymore."

This was the beginning of Theresa's journey. Theresa has a spirit guide that helped her hone her abilities. *As mentioned before,* her name is Kia. Theresa would consult with Kia to help her tap into her clients' spirit guides. It was so cool to watch her gaze upward to the right as she looked at Kia for help. To me, it looked like Kia probably floated in midair, but I never asked Theresa and she never offered me an explanation. Theresa later told me it was like Kia was downloading information into her brain.

I believe Theresa has helped countless people just like me, both dead and alive. Once she perfected her abilities, she became a counselor. The most recent thing Theresa shared with me was that a spirit kept waking her up at night, usually around three in the morning. *The witching hour.* That's when the veil between our world and the next is at its thinnest, thus making it easier for spirits to come through. For me, it's much easier for them to come to me in my sleep. I know I'm not as gifted as Theresa, and I doubt if I ever will be. That's probably a good thing, though. I can barely handle the abilities I do have. I'm blessed to know Theresa. If I ever have a problem or need some guidance through this crazy life of mine, I know she will always be there . . . in this world, or the next. She has taught me a lot.

My meeting with Theresa ended after a fast hour. My head was swimming. It usually takes me awhile to digest everything. So much information flooding my mind and blowing me away all at the same time. It's helpful to meet with someone who just gets it. I used to feel so alone with my abilities, and Theresa has helped me more than words can say. She's so relaxed about all the things that completely freak me out. I'm learning so much and trying to stay calm.

At least the activity has finally calmed down in our home. I'm just waiting for the next moment when all hell breaks loose again. I sense it's coming sooner than I realize. That's the scary part about being intuitive. I just sense things, and most of the time I'm right.

29

"So, how was your meeting with Theresa today?"

"Amazing, as usual."

"Is there anything you want to share with me?"

"Not really, maybe later if something comes to me. You know how my head is always swimming after meeting with her. I can't explain it, but I'm usually exhausted after only an hour. I wonder if it wears her out, too."

"I guess you'd have to ask Theresa."

Jeff was always polite when asking about my visits with Theresa. In all honesty, I don't think he could care less. I know he doesn't believe in any of this woo-woo stuff.

I prepared an early dinner so Stephanie wouldn't be late for softball practice. I was hurrying to set the table when my phone rang. I followed the sound of my phone and found it stuck between the couch cushions. I finally answered it on the fourth ring.

"Hello?"

All I could hear was a lot of heavy static and buzzing sounds. I couldn't make out a single word coming from the other end.

"Excuse me, hello? I think we have a bad connection. I can't hear you."

I heard a bit more static, then nothing. I thought I might have heard a faint voice, but it sounded like it was coming from really far away.

"I'm sorry, can you please call me back? I think there's something wrong with our connection."

When I hung up, I turned my phone over to check the caller ID. All it said was, "Out of area."

"Who called?"

"I don't know. There was too much static to hear what they were saying, and the caller ID said it was out of area."

"Weird, ok, let's not worry about it and eat. I'm sure if it's important they'll call back."

The next day I got another strange phone call. This time I could clearly hear what they were saying, even though it still sounded like it was coming from far away.

"I won't be making dinner."

When I asked who it was, the phone went dead. It sounded like a woman's voice, but again, the voice was so muffled and distant I couldn't recognize it. What's even more intriguing; when I checked the caller ID this time, "not in service" was all it said.

Two hours later, my friend Kerry called.

"Julie, I don't know how to tell you this, but I just found out Maggie was killed in a car accident."

"Oh my God, Kerry, when did that happen? I just talked to her a couple days ago when she invited us over for dinner."

"I know, Julie, *Kerry was so upset she could barely speak,* they had invited us over for dinner, too."

"How's her family doing? Her husband must be beside himself."

"Well, that's the next thing I need to tell you. Mitch was in the car with Maggie, and he didn't make it, either."

After I hung up the phone, it hit me. The phone call from earlier? I know it was Maggie who called me. *How the hell?* Maybe it's just the advancement in technology. I've heard people can record spirit voices on audio recorders, even though I've never been brave enough to try it myself. Will advancements in technology make it possible for the deceased to someday communicate with us?

Anything is possible.

I know I received a phone call from beyond the veil, even though I can't explain how it happened, I just know. Whether there's a logical explanation, or not, my friend Maggie still reached out. My only regret is that we couldn't have talked longer. All she said was, "I won't be making dinner." It's ok, Maggie, I'll take a raincheck. Add Maggie to the long list of people I've known who died too soon. As tragic as it is losing them both, I'm just glad they are still together and didn't leave any children behind.

Later that night I went to bed and cried myself to sleep over the loss of my friends. When I woke, I was standing on the dirt path inside the nearby forest. How in the world did I get here? I've never walked in my sleep before. I'm also not taking any sleep medications that sometimes cause people to sleepwalk. I should take sleeping pills because I don't sleep well at all these days. My doctor even prescribed something to help me sleep, but I'm too afraid to try it.

I know I'm awake this time. First of all, I heard a loud whistle from the nearby train tracks. Then, I pinched myself extra hard so I could be absolutely certain I was awake. My dreams are incredibly real these days, so I had to do it. Good thing I sleep in sweats. I can't imagine waking up from sleepwalking through my upscale neighborhood bare-ass naked.

I was standing there, completely alone in the middle of a very dark forest, but I wasn't afraid. I was more perplexed at how I got here than anything else. I was still deep in thought when I saw six bright lights that looked like car headlights a fair distance in front of me. My first thought was that these were definitely car headlights, but then I realized cars can't drive in the woods, and these lights were spread too far apart. They were bright white and looked like floating light bulbs. They faded to a light orange color, and then they started moving closer toward me.

I stood there completely transfixed on the incredible light show in front of me. The lights quickly turned to bright orange and were moving closer by the second. I was beginning to feel a little frightened, but way too curious to run away. It was like having a devil on one shoulder and an angel on the other. The angel was telling me to run, but the devil was telling me to stay. I agreed with the devil.

As the lights grew closer an amazing thing happened. The lights were dancing around until they lined up in a perfectly straight line. The orange lights were a perfect round orb and I was convinced I saw something forming inside of them. I'm straining my eyes, but I just can't get close enough to make out what was in there. I could try to walk closer to them, but I feel like I'm frozen in my spot. I don't think I could break free to run at this point if I had to.

Then, right before my eyes I saw the orange orbs had morphed into six Indians wearing large feather headdresses. Two Indians ran and hid behind a tree. I struggled to imagine how they could possibly fear me. I was too concerned with how afraid I was of them. Then I remembered my dream with the guardian Indians. I calmed down enough to look for a message.

One of the Indians had the brightest aura around him I've ever seen. My eyes were drawn to him. He pointed at something on the ground, yet he never said a word to me. I was surprised to find a shiny gold object laying in the dirt. I don't remember seeing it there before, even though it was only steps away from where I was. I walked over and picked it up. It looked like a beautifully ornate antique gold pocket watch. It appeared to be in excellent condition, even though it was weather-worn and dirty. I instinctively knew there was a definite meaning to this pocket watch. So, I reached down and picked it up. I looked back at the Indian, but he wasn't there anymore. All the other Indians had disappeared, too.

It hit me how freezing cold I was. It was such an eerie feeling standing there alone in the middle of a dark forest. When the Indians weren't there, the forest gave off a much creepier vibe. Funny how I didn't feel this way before. Maybe the Indians had some magical way of keeping me calm. I'm not feeling so calm anymore, I'm feeling panicky. I knew I had to get out of there. A strange sense of danger came over me. I'm struggling to calm my mind, but it won't go away. Fight or flight, that's what panic attacks are all about. My ever-growing fear was taking over. It's hard to get your footing on an uneven dirt road when you can't see anything. I made my way as quickly as I could back to the main road. I didn't have a watch on, so there's no telling what time it was. I wouldn't be able to see the time even if I had a watch. I was in pure blackness inside a dark and creepy forest.

I was relieved when I finally saw the glow of the streetlights ahead of me. I hope I never sleep walk again. I believe the spirit world influenced me to sleep walk until I woke up in the forest. *But why?*

When I finally arrived back home, I was happy to see I hadn't disturbed anyone. Jeff and Stephanie were fast asleep in their beds, none the wiser. I was also relieved because how in the world could I possibly explain this to them. I'm so intrigued by the forest. There's an amusement park on the outskirts of our town called, "The Enchanted Forest." I feel this place is also enchanted. I want to learn more about the graves and what those lights were all about. Maybe the pocket watch is a clue. A clue to what, though? I was definitely spiritually led to find it, that I know for certain. Living here feels like a million tiny puzzle pieces that only I can put together. I hope someday I can solve this mystery. I just pray I don't die trying.

I found my watch sitting on the table next to the couch. I picked it up and saw the time was four-thirty in the morning. Makes sense, the witching hour is three, the time when the veil between our world and the next is the thinnest. I wouldn't be at all surprised if my sleep-walking journey began at exactly three in the morning.

I was exhausted, so I tried to get a little sleep before the alarm went off. I fell asleep fast and began dreaming again. My two Indians were back. They didn't scare me this time, I was actually happy to see them. I needed answers. They must have read my mind because one of them answered my question before I could even ask it.

"Yes, we led you into the forest. We wanted you to find the pocket watch. Hold on to the watch. You will understand more later. It will connect you to what you need to know."

Before they left, they shared something incredibly tragic with me. They gave me a glimpse into some of my own family history that I never knew about. My ancestors fought against theirs many years ago in a distant past. I'm sure my parents don't even know about this. I was completely blown away.

"We will call upon you again, soon. We need your help to heal the land for both our tribes. Peace can finally come to this area. We have been waiting a very long time for you to arrive."

It appears they confirmed my worst fears. Our neighborhood really is built on ancient Indian burial grounds. This land was intended to be spiritually protected and sacred. It's been documented that tribes also used curses to protect their territory and harm their enemies. Could this land be cursed? I suspect it is. I totally blamed my old bitch of a neighbor, Donna. Maybe it wasn't her after all.

"We hope you will take on this significant task and help us. We will need you to find a shaman. The shaman is necessary to perform an ancient ceremony using tobacco. We need this ceremony to heal the land and honor our Indian ancestors."

I was so surprised at what they were saying to me, I don't remember if I even responded. Unfortunately, before anymore conversation could take place, my alarm clock blared, and I jumped off the couch. I can't begin to imagine what they meant when they said it somehow connects our ancestors. I will try to get to a library and do some research. Not that I have much hope for finding anything there. I know, maybe I can find a local tribe to help me. There's an Indian school not too far from my house. Maybe I should go there for answers. I don't even know what tribe these Indian spirits belong to. I should probably find that out as well. I would imagine the shaman needs to be from their tribe.

This is getting very interesting . . .

I couldn't wait to get started on my research, but I had other responsibilities today. Stephanie had just started taking pitching lessons, and it was my turn to drive her to her lesson. I'm not looking forward to it, not because I don't support my daughter, it's because I'm a klutz when it comes to anything sports-related. I'm so terrible at throwing a ball, and her teacher always makes fun of me. I'm extremely left-handed. I catch and throw with my left hand. Stephanie's teacher finds this hilarious, so he directs everyone's attention to watch me when I throw.

Plus, these girls, even though they are only in middle school, can throw a ball incredibly hard.

At least it's a sunny day, it's a beautiful drive to McMinnville. Her teacher teaches pitching in a barn out in the country outside of a little town called McMinnville. My four cousins used to live there. Our nickname for the town was, "Hickey McMickey." It's a very cute and quaint little town. My uncle is the one who worked at the rock crushing quarry that is now a man-made lake in my neighborhood. He worked there a long time.

We got to the pitching lesson and one of their goats came up to the fence to greet us. I call Stephanie the "animal whisperer." She's so amazing with animals and they are naturally drawn to her. Even wild animals. One time a deer brought her babies right up to Stephanie. It was incredible. Then the mother laid down next to Stephanie and allowed her to pet her. She even let Stephanie touch her face. The animals must sense they are safe around Stephanie. I've never seen anything like it. Anyway, Stephanie's coach lives on a farm and they had a lot of farm animals. They convert the barn into a school during the day. It's the perfect place for Stephanie, animals and softball.

"Hey Julie, ready to catch for Stephanie today?" Her teacher said, smirking.

"Not really."

"Well, we've been anxiously waiting for your arrival." *Wink, wink.*

"Cool." *Add an eye roll nobody can see.*

"Hey Carter, who's the new farmhand?"

"What are you talking about, Julie?"

"That guy standing in the pasture with your cows. I don't recall ever seeing him before."

"What guy?"

"There's a guy wearing striped overalls standing in your field next to the cows. He's looking straight at us. As a matter of fact, he just smiled and waved at you."

"Sorry Jules, there's nobody there."

"Mother! I need to get to my pitching lesson and I need you to catch for me."

"OK sorry, sorry."

Shit, I must have seen another spirit and didn't know it. Usually they are see-through, which is how I know they're spirits. This time the person was solid. I've also never seen a spirit outside of my house before, well, that I'm aware of. Stephanie gave me the, "Shut up, mother" look all middle school girls are known for. I swear, the older she gets, the stupider I get. Just the other day I was pulling in front of her school to drop her and her friend Jamie off. Jamie is her new best friend from down the street. Stephanie asked me to let them out in the parking lot next to the school from now on. It's not like I drive a crappy car like Jamie's dad does. I guess they just don't want their friends to know they have parents, anymore. Maybe it was the accident I got into last week in front of the school that embarrassed her. It wasn't even my fault. One of the other parents rear-ended me. I think it was because I drove her to school still wearing my sweats and slippers that freaked her out. *So what?* Just because I got out of the car to exchange information with the other driver in my sweat pants shouldn't be that big of a deal.

I miss that little girl who used to idolize and worship me. Will she ever come back? Now I'm just her chauffeur, errand runner, and supplier of funds. My friends with older kids tell me this is nothing. "Just wait until she turns fifteen," they all say. A girl going through puberty is no easy feat. I wonder who it's harder on, them or their mothers. Don't get me wrong, I love her to pieces. I just look forward to the day when I'm not such an embarrassment to her. Heaven forbid any of her friends find out I have abilities. I came way too close to blowing it at her coach's farm. I will be more careful next time. I wonder, are my abilities growing? How is it I am now seeing spirits the same way I see normal people? I will have to remember to talk to Theresa about this the next time I see her.

"Mom, what happened to you when we got to my lesson? There wasn't anyone in the field, and I was really embarrassed."

"Sorry hon, I really thought I saw a man out there. I promise to be more careful next time."

"I don't want any of my friends to know about this or anything that has happened in our house, ok? Promise me you won't tell anyone."

"I promise I won't. I completely understand. I didn't want my friends in high school to know I had abilities, either. But, listen Steph, I'm really not trying to upset or embarrass you. I'm really not. You're my only child and I love you the most. Please try to be a little more understanding. I'm not trying to cause you any problems, ok?"

"Yeah, ok mom, I get it. I guess I'm just worried about being bullied again."

"I promise you, I'm never going to let that happen. You have my word. Now let's put all this behind us and go get some ice cream, deal?"

"Double deal, mama."

Oh look, I'm mama again. Music to my soul.

30

I started hearing a girl crying. Not a young girl as in a child, but a younger girl perhaps in her early twenties. I searched all over the house for her, even called out to her, but I got nothing more in return. Sometimes sounds from outside can make it seem like it's coming from inside our house. I went outside and walked around the house to see if I could hear anyone crying outside, but still nothing. It began with just randomly hearing a girl crying here and there, and then it invaded my dreams. I have a feeling this might be connected to my Indians and that mystical forest nearby. I don't have any concrete reason for thinking that, it's probably just intuition. I also refer to my intuition as my "gut." I always make it a point to listen to my intuition. If I ever ignore my gut, I usually regret it.

Before I went to sleep that night, I asked my Indians to give me a sign. I'm hoping they can tell me what's going on. They did so much more, they gave me a vision.

In my vision, I saw myself in the hall bathroom rinsing my face in the sink. When I raised my head to look in the mirror, what I saw wasn't me. It was the face of a beautiful girl with dark hair. She was young looking, I would guess in her mid-twenties. She was wearing a white gown and I could see a few blood smears on her face. Off in the distance, I heard the crying sounds again, and I knew it was coming from the girl in the mirror. Then, I started hearing the brass shower curtain rings moving back and forth across the rack.

When I looked back in the mirror, it had completely fogged up. There wasn't enough hot water running to fog it up that much. I tried to wipe it off so I could see the girl's face again, but the fog completely hid her. I stood there wondering what to do next when the mirror instantly cleared up, and the shower curtain stopped moving. I looked in the mirror again, and this time I could barely see her face. Now it was more of a distorted face, not the beautiful dark-haired girl from before. I could see her slowly moving closer toward me. That's when I noticed her eyes. They were pained and panicked. Her eyes were so big and bulging I could barely see her eyelids. She was now dirty and had blood dripping down her face. She was trying to tell me something, but I couldn't understand what she was saying. I think she was being blocked by something I couldn't see.

She stopped trying to talk. Instead, she turned and looked to her right as a man walked into the mirror and stood next to her. He was carrying a knife. He began stabbing this poor girl over and over again. I was about to look away when I noticed a shiny gold pocket watch hanging on a chain inside his jacket. I looked down at my hands and now they were covered in blood. I freaked out a little, reached over to turn on the bathroom light when suddenly, I found myself lying safely in my bed. I looked down at my hands and the blood had disappeared.

I think she had to show me what happened to her because she couldn't tell me. When I saw the pocket watch, I knew there was a connection between this girl, the pocket watch I found in the forest, and this man. I'm certain he was her murderer. I need to take the pocket watch to the local police. Problem is, how do I explain my vision to the skeptical police department?

Later that afternoon, I took my rather unique and unbelievable story with me to the police department. Luckily, the detective I talked to believed me when I handed him the pocket watch.

"Where did you find this?"

"I found it in a forest area near my house. I saw something shiny on the ground and when I picked it up, I discovered I was holding an antique pocket watch."

"And you're saying you had a dream? A man wearing this same pocket watch stabbed a girl?"

"Yes, that's exactly what I'm saying."

Here it comes. He's going to send me packing with a few choice words about how nutty I am. It shocked me to hear what he said instead.

"Amazing. I need to do some research, but I think I read something about this in the archives. It's a cold case from many years ago, but this really rings a bell with me. Give me some time and I will see what I can come up with."

It really surprised me I got as far as I did. At least I wasn't laughed out of the police department. Maybe people are more open to this stuff than I give them credit for. I certainly wouldn't expect a police officer to buy into any of this. Most of the time I can barely wrap my head around it all.

It didn't take long until detective Harrison called me with some incredible information.

"You're not going to believe this."

Bet I do.

"I'm dying to hear what you have to say. Obviously, you found something?"

"Oh yeah, I found a lot. I found a case from the late 1800s about the very first serial killer in our area. What's even more interesting is his calling card."

"Calling card? What's a calling card?"

"It's something serial killers leave behind to identify the victims as theirs. Kind of like taking ownership over the body. It's disturbing stuff. Technically, these psychos leave an object at the scene of their crime as a way of taunting police or claiming responsibility."

"Does this have something to do with the pocket watch?"

"Not only is it the calling card of the serial killer, he stopped the watch at the exact time of his victims' death."

"It's too bad this happened so long ago and this maniac can't be punished for his crime."

"Maybe he is being punished. Do you believe in 'divine justice'?"

"Yes, I certainly hope there is such a thing."

I never heard the girl crying again. I believe something evil came with the pocket watch and once I handed it over to the police, I never heard or saw the girl again. I'm hoping it brought her closure and some much overdue peace so she could move on. I wonder if she had been a lost spirit all these years, still trying to solve her own murder. What a remarkable feeling to help this spirit find closure. Divine justice? I really hope it's a thing. I really do.

My Indian spirits did not disappoint. Later that night, when I was asleep, they came to visit me again in my dreams. They congratulated me and told me my abilities are growing. I told them I had suspected as much when I saw a full-bodied spirit out in the field the other day.

"We have more information we need you to look into. This is the part that involves your ancestors, and ours. We are asking you to research the history of the White River Uprising and the Puget Sound War. This took place in Washington State during the mid-1800's."

Before I could respond, the sound of the front doorbell ringing interrupted me.

Not this again.

As I approached the front door, I heard the door handle rattling as if someone on the other side was trying to open the door. Jeff also woke up and ran into the room.

"Who is here bothering us at three in the morning?"

Three . . .

"Jeff, go call 911. I'm not opening that door until the police get here. They are trying to turn the door handle to get inside. I'm not comfortable with what's happening here."

Jeff ran and grabbed my cell phone off the table next to the couch. He picked up the phone and to his amazement, 911 had already been called. The 911 operator was on the other end of the phone saying, "911, what's your emergency? Hello, hello is anyone there?"

"Yes, we need police, someone is trying into break in our house."

"We have dispatched police already and they are on their way. Would you prefer I stay on the line with you until they arrive?"

"Yes, please."

Within minutes, two police officers arrived.

"Police! Stop running and put your hands up."

We could hear a shuffling sound coming from the front door. I glanced out the side window above the kitchen sink in time to see both officers running around the side of our house. I assumed the person was trying to get away. I wonder how they got inside our back yard so fast. Jeff padlocked our fence shut. It's a very tall fence, too. There's no way anyone could have climbed it that fast.

The officers were out of breath when they came back around to the front of our house.

"As far as we can tell, there wasn't anyone at your front door when we arrived. We thought we saw a shadow or a figure of someone when we walked up the driveway, so we yelled out to it. Turns out we were mistaken. We looked everywhere and not a soul is on your property. Call us if you have any more issues."

The knocking, ringing and door handle movements all came to an abrupt end when the police arrived. Perhaps they saw a shadow figure. Something was there, Jeff and I both heard it. I'm pretty sure I already know what it is, but convincing Jeff of that was another thing. This was just the beginning of the fun we were about to have over the next few weeks.

Night after night, at exactly three in the morning it started up all over again. Same thing, even the 911 calls originating from my cell phone. The police were getting annoyed with us. I saw some of their reports and they all ended with the word, "again."

There were some other mystery 911 calls that originated from our house. That was the thing I found most intriguing. Calls going out on my cell phone that I never made. I asked if I could listen to some of the recordings and they actually let me. It was so strange. It sounded like a lot of muffled voices coming through from our end. Nobody at the police station could make out what the voices were saying. I don't think any of the officers believed me when I told them I never made any of those calls. They warned me to stop with a few threats thrown in. How do I stop doing something I've never done?

I need to find a way to put an end to this. I don't want to be in trouble with the police department. I'm sure my neighbors were more

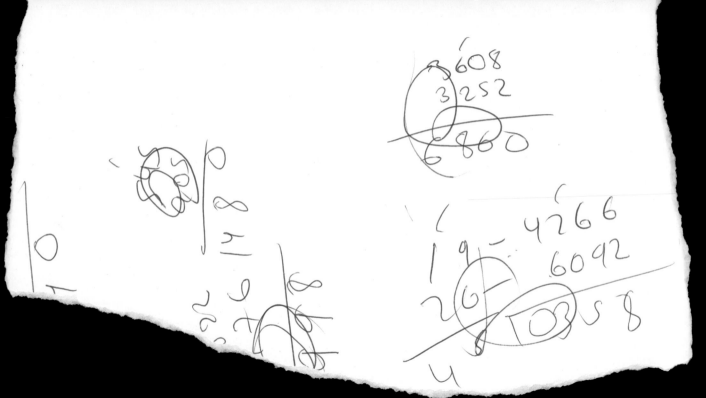

than sick of hearing police sirens in the middle of the night. So, the following night, I politely asked whatever spirit was causing the commotion to please stop.

"Please give us a break. I'm beyond exhausted, and it's not helping me figure out what you need. I want to help you, so if you can, please ask the Indian spirits guarding my coat closet to assist you. If they can't help you, they will give me the message you're trying to convey. Thank you and blessed be."

It worked, and the late-night activity completely stopped. I didn't hear another doorbell ringing at three in the morning, and the 911 calls stopped, too. I never found out what the spirit or spirits needed or wanted to tell me. Even though none of us could make out what the voices were trying to say, they sounded so frantic. Whatever it was, I hope they eventually found some peace. Deep down, I believe my Indian spirits were probably able to help them.

I sure hope so.

31

A month had passed since our three in the morning mystery visitor went away. I wonder if I will ever figure out who, what, or why it happened. I believe it was a spirit, or spirits trying to get my attention. The most frustrating part was not being able to understand what they needed. I have many theories, but nothing concrete. My first theory is the spirits from the cemetery want to be noticed. I hope in time I can figure it all out.

My priority right now is taking care of my Indian spirits request. They asked me to do some research on the White River uprising of 1855. I'm curious how this involves my ancestors, so I'm anxious to get to work. This is a story I definitely want to learn more about. What I found completely blew me away. I'm still shocked by what I discovered.

According to my resource, "Legends of America," it took place in Washington State and was known as, "White River Uprising." It was a battle between the Indians east of the Cascade Mountains, American soldiers and settlers igniting what has come to be known as, "The Puget Sound Indian War."

A statute was enacted in the 1850's by the United States Congress, known as the "Donation Land Act." They wanted to promote homestead settlements in the Oregon Territory. The problem was, the Indians were already residing on this land. The government gave white settlers free land where thousands of Indians were already living. Treaties were made and never honored by forcing the Muckleshoot people into starvation. This motivated them to take revenge. They attacked a settlement, killing at least nine people. William Brannan, (here's where it gets weird) his wife and child counted among the dead. William's brother Joseph took revenge and killed at least nine natives in an act of vengeance.

My mother's maiden name is Brannan. When the Indians mentioned my ancestors had something to do with theirs, they were right. I'm related to both William and Joseph. This didn't just involve the Muckleshoot Indians, however. Nisqually, Puyallup, and Klickitat Indians were also part of the Puget war in the Puget Sound area of Washington State. A lot of bloodshed is tied to this land. A beautiful area, but there's a lot of sadness to it. This land is so spiritually charged with trapped energy from all the traumatic events and tragic deaths that took place there. Where there's tragedy, there's going to be spirits.

The settlers who forced the Indians off the land had no compassion for Indians, and a lot of them starved to death. They took people's land away but worse, many lives were lost. I believe my Indian spirits need my help as a direct descendant to put an end to the war and heal the land. *Spirits are still angry.* They slaughtered entire families. I can't imagine. I'd be angry, too. Hundreds, possibly thousands of people lost their lives.

As far as I can tell, Joseph wasn't charged with anything criminal for the killing of at least nine Indians. To my surprise, it was his girlfriend who motivated him to stop killing. Her name was Sarah. She told him she'd leave him if he didn't stop. He didn't want to lose her, so he stopped killing. They married and lived out the rest of their lives as farmers. It's so freaky weird learning about all this. I'm just not sure if, or how, I can help the Indians. I know my ancestors were involved, but that was a really long time ago. What could this possibly have to do with me, and why now? All these years later, in my time and in my city. I live in Oregon, this happened far away up in Washington State. I'm hoping in time my Indians will explain it all to me. Perhaps I'm just feeling afraid and inadequate. I definitely struggle with self-esteem issues, so why not feel incapable. It's pretty much my modus operandi.

I learned I have another colorful ancestor, also with the last name of Brannan. His name was Sam. He was the very first millionaire in California history. He discovered gold in the Sacramento River. I thought he was a pretty savvy entrepreneur. Instead of risking his own life mining for gold, he sold mining equipment to the miners. He had a colorful life from what I've read. I'd love to visit Sacramento sometime to learn more about him. He's famous there, even today. There's a bar in Old Town Sacramento named, "Brannan Manor" in honor of him. They even displayed his picture on the wall. What a lovely way to pay tribute to good ole' Sam. I read a book about him that said he died penniless from too much gambling, wine, women and song.

That sounds about right for a relative of mine.

I think I get my entrepreneurial spirit from Sam. I'm glad that's all I inherited from him. I also read that he came to the west with his good friend Brigham Young. Sam was eventually kicked out of the Mormon religion.

Like I said, colorful guy.

There's another interesting family story about a crazy great grandmother. She lived in an old shack down by a river. She was very wealthy, but she believed money was the root of all evil. I heard she buried a lot of money on her property. Bummer nobody knows where she lived. I would love to find this fortune, but I doubt it even exists. *Who knows?* I swear, real life is so much stranger than fiction. I mean, seriously, you just can't make this stuff up.

It was 3:30 on a sunny Friday afternoon when I first started finding random pennies lying around the house. It started in the kitchen, then moved into the hallway. I remember thinking about the paranormal investigators' story about a penny falling from the ceiling and hitting one of them on the shoulder. Since they never returned any of my calls, I decided they were colossal frauds and paid no attention to it. Now I'm wondering if they were actually telling me the truth. I decided to do some more research. I'm getting a lot of experience at being a researcher. Luckily for me, I enjoy looking things up. Sometimes it can be eye opening, but in this case it was both fascinating and a little bit scary. I learned that it was an ancient Greek tradition to place coins on the eyes of the dead. This helped transport them across the river Styx to the land of the dead. Maybe it means nothing. It's probably just a myth, but I found it fascinating.

A few days later, we had a freak thunder, lightning and hail storm. It's rare to have storms like this in late April. I was just starting to make dinner when the lights flickered, then entirely went out. Jeff and Stephanie hadn't come home yet. Stephanie was at her softball practice and Jeff was on his way to pick her up. I sure hope they are safe inside his car right now. As for me, I needed to find a flashlight. I opened the cupboard where we usually kept it. I was so relieved when I reached down on the bottom shelf to find our flashlight was still there. We have the big industrial kind that throws off a ton of light. I don't like being alone in this house under normal conditions, but it was terrifying to be here alone in total darkness. It was incredibly eerie. Thank God for industrial flashlights.

The moment I turned it on, I heard a coin fall on the wood floor behind me. I reached down and picked up a penny. I know there weren't any pennies sitting on the kitchen counter. This one came out of nowhere, and I even heard it hit the floor. All the other times I just happened upon it, not knowing how *it* got there. Pennies falling from above. Hey, how about some hundred-dollar bills next time?

I joke when I'm nervous.

Another penny just fell on the stove. This time it made a different *tink* sound. I looked down to find a strange looking, *much larger* silver coin sitting on the counter. It's not perfectly round, either. It appeared to be hand struck and quite old. It had a profile of a face wearing an Indian headdress on one side and a horse with wings on the other. Another silver coin fell nearby, and this one had an eagle on it instead of a winged horse. I've never seen anything like this before. Jeff dabbles in coins, and from what I can tell, these are ancient silver. It didn't seem real. I felt like I should be dreaming, but I knew I wasn't dreaming. I pinched my arm though, just to be certain.

Then, the home phone that was mounted on the wall began ringing. How in the hell is that phone ringing? We disconnected it months ago. We had no use for it since we all have cell phones. We hadn't gotten around to dismantling it yet, but it wasn't plugged in. *How can it be ringing?* A moment later the electricity came back on and every appliance in the kitchen came to life. The food processor sitting on the counter was running at full speed. The toaster was going up and down, even the microwave timer was going off.

I turned to look at the microwave when something else caught my attention first. The chandelier in the entryway was swinging back and forth in a pretty intense way. Seconds later, the lightbulb inside of it exploded into tiny little pieces all over the slate floor. I was freaking out, but that wasn't even close to the worst thing that happened, not by a long shot.

I walked back to the kitchen after surveying the mess in the entryway. The microwave timer was driving me crazy, but no matter what I tried, I couldn't turn it off. Everything was going nuts in my house all at the same time. The television started turning on and off on its own, and then the kitchen lights followed. Not all the lights, just the ones hanging over the table where we eat our meals. The canned lights in the ceiling in the kitchen stayed on. I looked over at the TV and it was back on, but not on any particular channel, all I could see was static. It was incredibly loud, too. As I reached to turn down the volume, something else caught my eye.

I looked at the television and in the middle of the screen I could see a face with horns coming out of its head. This thing had two sets of horns. One set looked just like ram horns that curled and the other set looked like antelope horns that stood straight up on top of its head. I knew instantly, this is a demon. I was completely transfixed on the demon inside my television, unable to take my eyes off of it when suddenly, it just disappears.

At the same time, a foul smell blew through the room. It was a cross between rotten eggs and rotting flesh. I remember smelling this gross smell before. It blew past me like a disgusting wind. Luckily, it dissipated after a few minutes. A few very long minutes. I began hearing loud, angry voices and banging sounds coming from all around me. It sounded like people were bouncing off the walls in the hallway, but I couldn't see anyone. I felt like I was in the middle of some kind of battle, even though I knew I was completely alone. It gradually advanced to where I was hearing women screaming and people scrambling around as if they were trying to escape. I was about to run out the door when it abruptly stopped. It was like someone had flipped a switch, it was over that quickly. I sat down on the couch in a state of total bewilderment.

I was trying to process it all when the kitchen faucet turned on at full blast. I got up, walked into the kitchen and shut it off. As I turned to leave, the water came back on at full force.

"Stop it, God damnit it, just stop it! Leave me the fuck alone, you disgusting, filthy evil spirit. Get the hell out of my house. You're not welcome here."

I was totally freaking out. I shut the water off again, and as I turned to walk back into the family room, the demon from inside my television was now standing right in front of me. I let out the loudest scream. I mean, even I was surprised I could scream like that. It was more like a primal scream coming from deep down inside my soul. I was absolutely horrified. When I finally stopped screaming, the demon just stared at me in the most sinister way. Then he grinned, showing its long, razor-sharp teeth. Its eyes were bright, almost blinding, and glowed blood red. I could feel some deep, painful scratches, ever so slowly stinging down the back of my neck. I found my inner strength and pulled away from its mental grasp. I took off running as fast as I could and headed toward the back door. I looked behind me when I got to the end of the hallway. To my relief, it hadn't followed me. I opened the back door and ran into the garage.

Pretty sure my plan was to keep running.

I opened the automatic garage door just in time to see Jeff and Stephanie in the driveway. It was at that moment when I realized I hadn't even finished making dinner for them yet. I need to pull myself together. The last place in the world I wanted to go was back inside that house. I should have told Jeff exactly what was going on, but I didn't think he would believe me. I was probably still in shock. Nobody makes good decisions when they're in shock, especially me. I should have grabbed my family and insisted we leave, just like our neighbors did. But that's not what happened.

"Julie, what's going on? You're white as a sheet."

"Or, one might even say, white as a ghost?"

"Not this again. Did something else happen?"

"Um, well yeah. *Duh.* I really need to talk to you. I know you're probably going to judge me and call me crazy, but this shit is really happening."

"I don't want you to talk about it now, especially not in front of Stephanie."

"Fine, but we definitely need to talk. It can wait until after she goes to bed. That is, if the house doesn't blow up before then."

Jeff walked away. I'm a freaking nervous wreck and he just walks away.

"We are having takeout tonight."

I needed a reason to get out of the house for a while. Let Jeff deal with whatever happens while I'm away. Secretly, I really wished something would happen when Jeff was home alone. It rarely does anything when Jeff is here. Quite the opposite, it always waits until I'm alone before it terrorizes me. It's always been this way. I wonder why I'm the only one who's targeted in our family. I'm relieved it's not Stephanie, that's for sure, but why me? Why me? *Why the hell me?* What did I ever do to deserve this?

I didn't wait for a response from Jeff. I grabbed my keys and got out of there. I don't know why I even bother telling Jeff anything. He's not going to believe me, anyway. I wish I could drive to the nearest bar and have a drink. *I'm so stressed out.* I can't drink anymore though, because of my stupid pancreas. Life just isn't fair sometimes, is it? I can't think of anyone on the planet who deserves a good stiff drink more than me right now.

I drove to the local pizza parlor and ordered a pizza. At least I could sit here and wait while they made it. I wish I could have just one beer to help me relax a little. I don't smoke anymore, either. I quit five years ago. But right now, I'd kill for either one.

When I got back home, Jeff was holding one of the silver coins that fell from out of nowhere.

"What is this?"

"That's what I wanted to talk to you about."

In my haste to leave, I forgot about all the coins that had fallen around the house.

"There's pennies all over the hall. Julie, why are there pennies all over the hallway?"

"I don't know."

"What do you mean you don't know?"

"Jeff, you will just have to wait until later. You didn't want me talking about it in front of Stephanie, remember?"

"Fine, let's just eat."

We sat down to eat pizza together and Stephanie had a few questions of her own I didn't know how to answer.

"Did something happen, Mom?"

"No sweetie. Everything's fine."

"Don't lie to me, I know when you're lying. Something happened, didn't it?"

"Yes, but it wasn't that big of a deal. Just thought I heard something, but it was probably just coming from outside."

"Fine, don't tell me."

I hate lying to her. It's more my nature to be completely honest with her. But this situation was different. It would terrify her if I told her the truth. I comforted myself with the knowledge nothing scary had happened to her yet. *Yet is the key.* I was worried it would start bothering her, but so far all she's heard are some scratching sounds, bangs from the dryer and her phone picked up on something when we first moved in. She's finally been able to put that all out of her mind, and I didn't want to drudge it back up for her. Her life is happy and she's made lots of new friends. Why burden her with this? If it wasn't affecting her, why tell her? I can barely explain it to myself. How in the world do I explain it to a child? Actually, she's almost a teenager. Time goes by so fast, doesn't it? Seems like just yesterday she was my sweet little toddler. Now I have a daughter going through puberty.

Stephanie was tired from her softball practice, so shortly after dinner she decided to go to bed a little early. When I was sure she was fast asleep, I decided it was time to have a little chat with Jeff.

"Jeff, I really need to talk to you. Is now a good time? I believe Stephanie's asleep and won't hear us."

"Now is as good a time as any."

"I don't know how to say this, but Jeff, I think I saw . . ."

"What?" *Long pause for dramatic effect.*

"I think I saw a ghost. Sorry, that's not exactly true. I don't think I saw it, I know I did. Never mind, that's not true either, it wasn't a ghost I saw, it was a demon."

Crickets.

"Jeff, I really think we should move."

"There's no way we're selling this house. We will lose our shirts if we sell now."

"Ok great, let's just risk my life instead. I'm really afraid something here is out to hurt me."

"Sorry Julie, but someone's got to be the voice of reason in this family."

"You think I'm a crazy lunatic, don't you? This IS happening. There is definitely something evil inside our house. Just because it hasn't attacked you yet, don't be so sure it won't. Voice of reason? You obviously don't give a crap about what I'm going through."

"Oh ok, we've gotten to the part of the conversation where I walk away."

"Well, at least you're extremely good at it. Walking away from me is what you do best."

"Julie, we are done having this conversation."

I kept my distance from Jeff the rest of the evening. I was so hurt and afraid we'd just keep arguing. Later that night, I cried myself to sleep. Sometimes I feel so desperate and alone. I don't know how much more of this I can take.

32

My nightmares returned later that night. My sleep was very restless, but that's nothing new. Whenever I'm feeling stressed, I have restless sleep. I dreamed I was a little girl again, sitting on the couch in the same home I grew up in. I can see what looks like the shape of a person walking toward me from the far end of a very long and dark hallway. As soon as they came into focus, it morphed into the scariest looking old hag witch type of creature. The skin was black and leathery. She was staring at me with these piercing eyes that were blacker than night.

I'm completely frozen. I can't scream, I can't cry, and worst of all I couldn't move. My legs and arms won't work. The moment the creature reached out to touch me, I woke up feeling like I'd just been electrocuted. It was freaky to experience the feeling of electricity flowing through me. It started in my head and came out my toes. I imagine this is what it feels like to be struck by lightning. I could even feel the electricity in the air. I've never felt anything like this before. Every time I fell back asleep, the dream started back up again. I wanted to blame all the stress I was under. Truth is, I'm really not sleeping very well anymore and I haven't in a long time. It's taking a physical and mental toll on me.

There's a difference between nightmares and spirit visits in my sleep. When I dream about someone visiting me, I instinctively know it's a visit from spirit. Same thing with my nightmares. I have a pretty cool ability that has really come in handy for me over the years. When I'm having a nightmare, I can warn myself inside the dream that it's just a bad dream and not to worry. I have even been able to wake myself up by doing this. It's like I come into my dream and console my dream-self and if necessary, pull myself out of it. Not this time though. I either couldn't get inside my dream or I was being manipulated by this thing and it blocked my ability to wake up.

It was incredibly unnerving.

I used to have recurring nightmares as a kid. It was always the same dream, too. In my dream my mother almost kills me. The dream goes like this . . . I'm in my bed which was straight down the hall from my parent's bedroom. I had just woken from a very scary dream and needed some comforting. After I checked under my bed for monsters, I got up and walked down the hallway toward their bedroom. When I got to their room, I stood inside the door and called out for my mother. She sat straight up in bed, scowled at me and said, "What do you want?" I answered, "Mommy, I'm scared, I had a really bad dream."

The only response I got was, "Go back to bed, or else."

I'm trying to move on the wood floor, but my socks are slipping and I'm going nowhere. I look over at my mother and she's coming at me carrying a butcher knife she pulled out from under her bed.

She yells at me to get out again. She's glaring at me with these black eyes that are darker than dark. She looks like pure evil and I begin to shake. I'm desperately trying to get away, but my socks continue to slip until I trip and fall on the hardwood floor. This is it, mom's going to kill me.

"I warned you to get out, and now you're dead. I'm going to enjoy cutting you up into tiny little pieces."

Demonic laughter fills the air.

It's at that same moment I wake up in my bed soaking wet with sweat. Every time it's the same scenario. What child under the age of nine dreams their mother is going to kill them? I had this nightmare frequently, too. I don't know what age I was when the dream started, but I was sure glad when it ended. I believe it was during these dreams when I learned to reassure myself that it wasn't real. Fortunately for me, I have been able to continue doing this into my adulthood.

My nightmare with the hag witch continued night after night for at least two weeks. One night the entity followed me out of my nightmare. I could feel the pressure of someone leaning in next to me. Not quite sitting, but almost. I opened my eyes and there it was. This time I didn't freak out and run away. I knew my fear would only give it more energy. Instead, I closed my eyes and cried out for help.

I am a child of God. Jesus, please come help me.
Saint Michael, I need you.
Please come fight for me.

I opened my eyes again, and the entity was gone. Then, a really remarkable thing happened. I felt like I was wrapped in warmth and love. A sense of peace came over me like never before. I could see lots of bright lights floating around the room, but I wasn't afraid, not even a little bit. All that fear I had inside of me was washed away. I knew I was in the divine presence of pure light. I felt like I had angels around me, protecting me from this evil. I knew my prayer was not only heard, it was answered in the most incredible way. I don't feel so alone anymore. No doubt in my mind, Angels saved me that night.

I really need to share this story with another person. I'm still angry at Jeff, so I gave Mary a call.

"Hey Mary, are you busy? I have something really cool I wanted to share with you. Would it be alright if I come over to your house?"

"Sure, I'm not at home right now, would you care if I came to your house?"

"Well, I need to talk to you about something that happened in my house last night. I'm really not comfortable talking about it here."

"I understand. I should be home shortly so come on over. By the time you get there, I should be home."

"Great, thanks Mary, I really appreciate it."

You have no idea.

I was becoming extremely paranoid talking about anything paranormal while still inside my home. I felt safer in every way outside of my house. I know others have told me it doesn't matter, but I feel like I'm being constantly watched these days. *These walls have eyes.* It sounds crazy, even to me, but it felt like the house itself was coming to life. Truth is, I wasn't safe discussing it anywhere.

"Mary, I don't even know where to begin."

"How about we sit down, drink a little tea and just chat first."

"That would be lovely."

"So, how is everyone?"

"Well, pretty sure Jeff thinks I'm a complete lunatic. Stephanie and I haven't been getting along as well lately, either. It feels like when we are in the house together, it makes us angry. I can't explain it, but the tension is incredibly thick."

"Julie, I think it's time. I need to go inside your home to see if I can get a feel for what's going on."

"Do you want me to tell you what's been happening? Or would you prefer I wait?"

"It's best if you don't tell me anything. I don't want to go in with any preconceived opinions and get it wrong. It's best for me to read your house cold."

"Ok, when do you want to come over?"

"No time like the present."

"You sure? You mean, right now?"

"You really are a procrastinator, aren't you?"

"Yes, but how did you know?"

"Your spirit guides are practically screaming it at me!"

I didn't know how to tell Mary that I was feeling apprehensive. Mary was incredibly gifted, and I wondered if she was taking too big of a risk coming over to my house. I was afraid something bad could happen to her.

"Mary, do you need to prepare before you go inside my home?"

"Don't worry Julie, I'm asking my spirit guides to protect me as we speak."

"Good idea. That place is getting scarier by the minute and I want you to be as prepared as possible. I believe something very negative is there."

As we got closer to my house, Mary said she could feel the vibration of something evil.

"Julie, I'm getting something from another dimension, another realm entered ours and now it's settled inside your home. Not just one, many. Are you aware that you have multiple spirits in your house? Not all of them are good, there are some that are very evil. I'd even go as far as to say there are demonic entities present."

"Wow Mary, that's impressive. I have no clue how you're able to do that. We aren't even inside my home yet. How did you do that?"

"Honestly, I have no idea. Don't tell anyone my secret, ok?"

"Ok, you got it. Makes perfect sense to me. I have no clue how I'm able to see spirits, either."

"I'm not at all surprised you have many spirits in your home. You have abilities, so you're like a beacon for the spirit world. I'm most concerned about the demonic presence I'm feeling, though. I'm going to gather some more protection before we go inside."

"Take all the time you need to gather extra protection. Can you please get some for me, too?"

Mary got out some different gem stones and blessed medals. I knew nothing about all the spiritual power that was held inside of a rock. I'm learning a lot about things I didn't even know existed. Sometimes I miss my peaceful, clueless little world.

"I think I'm about as ready as I'm ever going to be, let's go inside, shall we?"

I wanted to say no or enter at your own risk, but all I said was, "Ok."

I could feel my legs shaking as Mary and I made our way up the front walkway. I said a prayer inside my head before we made it to the front door.

"I didn't know you were religious."

"How in the world did you know I was saying a prayer?"

"Saint Michael told me."

"That's so cool!"

Mary never gave me an explanation about how Saint Michael told her I was praying. I've had to accept the fact that I have abilities, but

I'm nothing like Mary or Theresa. They blow me away. I'm forever in awe of their incredible abilities.

Mary stood silent for a moment after she walked inside the front door. I looked over at her and was surprised to see a worried look on her face. I felt both sorry and frightened for her. Obviously, she wasn't at all prepared for what she was about to find. Who in the world could have been? I certainly wasn't.

"Julie, have you had any neighbors move recently?"

"Yes, we've had a few."

"Well, you're about to lose another one."

At that moment, a moving van pulled up in front of our house. I knew it wasn't for us, even though I secretly wished it were.

"Our next-door neighbor must be moving again. This is the fifth family who's lived there. Nobody stays in that home for long. It's always up for rent. No tenants have lived there longer than a month since we've been here. One family left all their furniture and uneaten dinner sitting on the kitchen table."

"Wow, something powerful must be here and it's obviously not just affecting your house. There must be something tied to this land."

"That's exactly what I think. These homes are all brand new. We are the first family to live in our house."

Mary walked further inside, then she stopped in front of the coat closet.

"There's a portal inside the closet."

"Yes, I know, but I'm darn impressed you do, too."

"There's a powerful presence here. It wants you to know it's here. Have you been attacked in this house?"

"Yes, many times."

"There's a terrible evil here. So much hatred toward women. I've never felt anything like it. He's killed on this land before, and Julie, I believe he wants to hurt you. There are women spirits here who are protecting your daughter, but they can't protect you, too."

I'm relieved to know why Stephanie hasn't been affected like I have. I take comfort in knowing there are spirits here protecting her. I also have a hunch I know who the great evil is. I believe it's connected to the same person who left the pocket watch in the forest. Could this be the serial killer?

"What should we do, Mary?"

"You need to get out of this house."

"I'd love to go jump inside that moving van sitting outside, but we can't move. All our money is tied up in this house. I've begged Jeff so many times and every time the answer is no. At this point in time, there's no hope of changing his mind."

"Well, ok then, we will just have to do some intense cleansing of this home."

"Can you help me, Mary?"

"It will take more than I'm capable of handling alone. Don't worry, I know a group of women who are very skilled, but it's going to take some time and a lot of effort. You sure you can't just move? I'm not nearly as worried for anyone else here as I am for you. You could be putting yourself in some real danger by staying."

"I understand, but how in good conscience do I pass this problem on to another person? I really need to get rid of whatever this is. I couldn't live with myself if I put some unsuspecting, innocent person through the hell I've been through. It just wouldn't be right."

"I knew you were good people."

"Yeah, sure. Completely nuts is more like it."

"Hang on to your sense of humor. It will really come in handy over the next few weeks."

"Weeks? This is going to take weeks?"

"Don't worry Julie, I know some amazing women who can help. The first thing I want to do is bring in a paranormal team to try to get some evidence. It's important to learn as much as we can about the entities before we bring in the others."

"What others?"

"Let's see . . . we have a few mediums who specialize in different types of crossing over, a Reiki master and a shaman. I have a feeling you're going to need them all."

I wasn't too jazzed about having another paranormal team in here, but at least I'm confident these people are legit. I want to have faith that Mary knows what she's doing. I need to be able to believe in someone. At least she has lots of contacts in the paranormal world. I'm beginning to finally feel hopeful.

"Do you own any antiques?"

"Yes, we have a dresser that used to belong to Jeff's grandfather."

As soon as I said that, the door leading into the room where the dresser stood opened on its own.

"That's strange. That's one thing that hasn't happened here yet."

I walked over toward the room and Mary followed me.

"The dresser I was talking about is sitting against the back wall inside this room."

"Interesting."

"Julie, do you know anything about the person who owned it? Am I correct to assume he's passed away?"

"Yes, I believe he died a long time ago, long before Jeff and I met. I know nothing about him, but I'll ask Jeff later when he gets home from work."

"One last thing before I go. You need to try to make your relationship between you and Jeff more loving. There are entities here that want to destroy you. Don't allow it. When you start feeling anger building up remember to tell yourself it's not you. You are being influenced. Evil feeds on anger. Anger puts out a lot of energy. You're strengthening it by fighting. Just be aware and be careful. I believe what's here is very ancient and extremely powerful."

Ancient and powerful. I can't get those words out of my mind.

I like spending time with Mary, but I was relieved she had to go. Jeff would be home with Stephanie soon. I haven't mentioned the paranormal topic to Jeff in a while. Mary said if we fight anymore, it will only strengthen the negative entities. The only way I can accomplish that is by not talking to him about any of this stuff.

"Julie, I will be in touch soon. Don't forget to ask Jeff about that dresser."

As soon as Mary drove away and before I shut the front door, Jeff and Stephanie pulled in the driveway. He was actually in a good mood today, and so was Stephanie. She was excited for her very first little league game.

"Mom, guess what?"

"What, sweetie?"

"I get to be the starting pitcher tomorrow for our first game."

"Wow, that really is an honor. I'm so proud of you!"

She even ran over to me and gave me a big hug. I didn't realize how much I missed those hugs until now. Things had become so stressful. We all need a break, and that's exactly what I intend to do. I hope it lasts for more than a day, but you have to start somewhere. No way am I going to allow anything I can't see destroy this family. I'm finally feeling stronger and more powerful than I've ever felt before in this house. What a wonderful feeling and much overdue. We never really had a chance to relax and enjoy our new home.

I prepared my specialty for dinner, I'm not the greatest cook on the planet, but I do make a fabulous lasagna.

"Julie, you outdid yourself with dinner tonight. Both Stephanie and I want to thank you."

"Yes, thanks mama, it's super good."

"Well, what a treat, thanks to both of you for appreciating my hard work. I agree, it really is especially good tonight."

We sat down after dinner and played a few games of gin together. Stephanie killed us both. She usually always wins, and it's not because we let her. She's just superb at playing gin. It was such a fun night. My family desperately needed some togetherness. I'm happy to say, no spirit, and especially nothing evil interrupted us. Maybe they needed a break, too. Whatever the reason, I was grateful. We acted and felt like a normal family for a change. I will cherish this because there's no telling what tomorrow might bring.

After I put Stephanie down for bed, I asked Jeff about his grandfather. I'm not going to tell him why I'm asking. I'll just say I'm curious about the man. Who knows, maybe he'll be more open to talk about his grandfather as long as there wasn't a paranormal reason behind it.

Jeff was sitting on the couch watching television when I walked into the family room.

"Hey Babe, can I ask you a question?"

"Sure."

"It's about your grandfather. I know we were lucky enough to inherit his beautiful old dresser, but I just realized I know nothing about the man. Can you tell me what you know about him, or his life, when he was alive?"

"Oh wow, that takes me back. I never met the man. He died before I was born, but I've sure heard plenty of stories about him. From what I've been told, he wasn't a very nice person."

Ok, not even a little surprised to hear that.

"Well, just tell me what you've heard if you don't mind, and please don't leave anything out."

"Alright, where do I begin?"

"Why don't you start with his name."

"His name was Melbourne Floyd."

"Wow, his name alone makes him sound like some kind of gangster, perhaps someone involved in the mafia?"

"He was a professional gambler and bootlegger. Many in our family suspected mob ties because of his nefarious activities. He also owned a construction business in New York, which back in the day was controlled by the mob."

"Really? I was just joking, but go on."

"All I know is, his nickname was Al, and he was involved in a lot of bad things when he was alive. My father told me he was very cruel to him and his brother, and especially abusive to their mother."

"So, Al was your father's father. I always thought he was your moms."

"No, mom's father was a redheaded Irishman."

"Al sounds very colorful."

"My father said he wouldn't walk across the street for the man. He hated him. Dad told me during his life they had chauffeurs and servants. His father eventually gambled away all the money, and they ended up homeless and broke."

"I never knew any of this. Why have you never spoken of Al before? Any idea why we have his dresser in our home?"

"My father wouldn't allow it in his house. When I moved out my parents practically begged me to get it out of their garage."

"Wow, that's interesting. Mind if I ask why you took it? I mean, were you a little weirded out about using it since your father wouldn't even allow it inside his house?"

"It was free."

Oh yeah, that explains my husband. He is very successful and makes good money, but he's a major tight wad. He said we might have money today, but it could all be gone tomorrow. He never feels secure. I'm surprised he wanted to buy this house so badly. I believe it's his security. "Growing equity in a home will secure our future," Jeff always said. He has gone from rags to riches, then back to rags again. The business he's in can be extremely volatile. Janitorial contracts can end tomorrow, and then we'd be broke, just like his grandfather. Life can be scary and unsettling. I see some similarities in both Jeff and his grandfather, but for very different reasons. I'm focused on all the activity in our home. Jeff is primarily focused on keeping a roof above our heads. *Regardless of what's lurking beneath.* I give him credit, he's a very hard worker. I wouldn't be living in this neighborhood if it weren't for Jeff. Hopefully, we can find a way to stay. I'm putting a lot of my faith in Mary. I don't have any other options at the moment.

"Sounds like your grandfather was a very evil man."

"Yes, that's exactly how my father described him. He also referred to him as a son of a bitch. Let's just say, there was no love lost between the two."

I never told Jeff the real reason I was asking about his grandfather. I didn't want to ruin the perfect evening we were having. We all slept peacefully, too. It's very rare to have nights like this, especially lately. I wonder if Mary had a little something to do with that. I'd better call her and share what I learned about Jeff's grandfather. I'm sure she will be very intrigued when I tell her about it.

When I picked up the phone to call Mary, I heard Mary saying hello on the other end. Mary had called me at the same moment.

"Speak of the devil, I had just picked up my phone to call you."

"So, did you ask your husband about his grandfather?"

"Yep, and in a nutshell, his grandfather was not a good person."

I shared all the information with Mary. I had a feeling she wasn't at all surprised.

"Julie, I'm trying to contact my paranormal group. I haven't heard from them yet, but they were out on an investigation I couldn't attend last night. Is it alright if I make arrangements for them to come over to collect some evidence soon?"

"Yes, but I haven't mentioned any of this to Jeff yet. I was hoping to keep him out of it."

"We can come during the day when he's not at home if that's alright."

"I assumed since the last paranormal team came late at night your team would want to as well."

"I've captured some incredible evidence during the daytime. Ghosts were once people and people sleep at night. I always thought it was better to research during the daylight hours."

"That sounds great to me. I'm quite relieved I don't have to bring Jeff into this yet."

"I will set it up for some time during the day then. Is there any day or time that works best for you?"

"Mornings between eight and eleven are perfect. Stephanie's in school by then and Jeff would have already left for work."

"Ok, works for me. I will let you know when we can all get together. Julie, in the meantime, just keep saying your prayers and lean on your faith. We will sort this out, don't you worry. Just try to keep everything calm before we can get there. I will pray for you."

"Mary, can I ask you a question? Did you do anything to help us have the splendid night we had last night? We sat down together for dinner and after dinner we played a few games of gin. We hadn't played any games in a really long time. I also got a glorious night's sleep. I swear, I slept like I haven't slept in months."

"Glad to hear it! I might have added a little protection or two here and there. Be warned, it wears off fast so just be careful, ok?"

"You got it, Mary. I will do my best. Thanks so much for the wonderful night we just had."

"You're more than welcome. Hopefully, we can help you and your family have many more of those in the days to come."

And with that, Mary hung up. I'm feeling strangely alone again, but I can't understand why. I think I should get out of this house for a while. I deserve to have a little fun. I think I'll go to my favorite yarn store and buy some yarn to knit a sweater. Hopefully, by the time winter rolls around again, I will have finished it. I'm very experienced at crocheting, but still trying to teach myself how to knit. Knitting a sweater will be a challenge for me and will hopefully help me focus on something other than my house.

After I spent some quality time at the yarn store, I treated myself to lunch at my favorite restaurant. I haven't done anything fun like this in a really long time. It hasn't been that long since I quit my job. After Stephanie was so badly bullied at her last school, I was fortunate enough to be able to stay home, but I still get a little bored when nobody's around.

Today was a great day. *Rare for me.* The sun was shining, and it was beautiful outside. I took a stroll through town and checked out some dress boutiques. Everything was way out of my price range, but still fun to look. So much has been going on, I hadn't even bothered to familiarize myself with the town I'm now living in. Later, I went to my daughter's very first softball game. I was happy and proud as I watched Stephanie pitch her very first little league softball game. Her team won.

The perfect end to the perfect day.

33

I woke to the sound of my phone ringing. I can hardly believe it. I don't remember the last time I slept in. Jeff and Stephanie weren't even home. Looks like Jeff took Stephanie to school. Nice of him to let me sleep in. Things are finally beginning to look up for us, *I hope.*

"Julie? You alright?"

"Hey Mary, yeah, I'm fine. I slept in. I can't believe I slept in. This is incredible."

"Sounds like you needed it. Do you know it's already afternoon?"

"Gosh, no, I had no idea. I must be a teenager again."

"Did I wake you?"

"No, I had to get up anyway to answer the phone."

"Hilarious. At least you haven't lost your sense of humor."

"So, what's up, Mary?"

"I was just wondering when you'd like my group of investigators to come over."

"If it's alright, I'd still prefer to do this when nobody else is here. By that I mean Stephanie and Jeff. Jeff is such a skeptic and I don't want to risk anything scaring Stephanie."

"That's perfectly understandable. We have some time tomorrow if you're available."

"Tomorrow? I don't know if I'm ready, I'm panicking a little."

"What are you afraid of, Julie?"

"Everything."

"Don't worry. I have a caring group of ladies I'm bringing with me. You're in excellent hands. Can we come over tomorrow morning around ten?"

Gulp.

"No time like the present I always say!"

I never say that. I'm the world's biggest procrastinator.

"Great, see you then."

I spent the rest of the day cleaning the house. At least the spirits left me alone long enough to be presentable. I was so full of anticipation and excitement I could barely sleep. I don't know how I kept this from Jeff, but I did.

I dropped Stephanie off at school and went home to wait for my guests. Time dragged on until the clock struck ten.

I opened the door to find six smiling women standing in front of me.

"Please, come in."

Mary walked in first and introduced me to everyone. There was Jill, she's a medium, Connie, an EVP specialist, Janet, equipment specialist, Jennifer and Amy, both Reiki masters, and of course Mary who's both a medium and a shaman. All the women have very special abilities and they are part of the same paranormal investigative team. I felt this time would be different, I instantly trusted these women.

It took about half an hour for them to set up their equipment in different areas around the house. They took the time to explain each device to me. Janet was very knowledgeable about the equipment and did most of the talking.

"Spirits consist of energy which can be measured by electrical impulses."

It was incredibly interesting. They had digital voice recorders that captured spirit voices, also known as EVP, or electronic voice phenomenon. EMF meters, K2 meters, full-spectrum and SLS cameras.

Most of their equipment I've never heard of before, let alone know what it does. Mary told me the equipment is used to communicate with spirits because most people can't see or hear them.

I've never seen a rem pod before. Rem pods are a little more technical. They use a mini telescopic antenna to radiate an electromagnetic field around the device to detect spirit energy and various anomalies. It also has multi-colored lights and sounds that will alert you when ghosts are present. Basically, it's believed that spirit energy can manipulate the electromagnetic field. Meaning, if a spirit gets close to the rem pod, it will sound an alarm and LED lights will flash.

Fascinating!

The women split up into different rooms of the house. I could hear meters going off here and there, but nothing much happened on the level of activity. I'm not even a little surprised these entities are hiding. I was afraid this would happen. I even sensed this was the way it was going to go. I need to try harder not to lose faith. I trust Mary not to send me frauds. I need to forget the terrible experience I had with that last group and put it behind me. I need to believe in someone. What other choice do I have?

I was sitting in the living room waiting for the women to finish their experiments when I heard a recorder go off.

"Pray" was the only word that came through.

A few moments later I heard the voice recorder say "make an offering." The air in the house started warming up, so I went to check the thermostat. Jill walked by me and chuckled a bit.

"Evil entities can raise the temperature of the room, whereas ghosts usually cause cold spots."

"Jill, how do spirits cause cold spots? I've felt them so many times just randomly in my house. I've also felt chilly breezes blow across my face."

"If it's a ghost, it will pull energy out of the room, therefore making the air feel extremely cold. The spirits need energy to manifest."

As we stood together talking, we both felt a warm breeze and then came the putrid smell of rotting eggs. We just looked at each other. Jill was the first to break the silence.

"We are in the presence of something very evil. Follow me out of this room for a moment and let's see if it follows us."

Fortunately, it didn't follow us. I was pretty shook-up and Jill could see it.

"Julie, it's alright, we are going to do everything we can to help you. Please don't worry, you can trust us."

Jill just validated her psychic abilities to me. I'm feeling much more at ease with these women. Maybe I've finally found the group who can help me.

Another spirit came through on an EVP saying my name while mimicking my voice at the same time.

"Did I just hear the spirit who's been mimicking us?"

As soon as I asked, the same voice came through again and repeated my question.

Mary was quite intrigued and said, "There's your answer. I believe your intuition is correct. I'm still not sure if this is a spirit or a demon, so be careful as we move forward."

Mary is very intuitive, and it affected her the moment she stepped inside our house. I don't know how much evidence they collected, because I think most of the spirits here hid from them. Regardless, they could still sense what's here.

"Julie, there's a lot going on here. The oppressive energy is strong, can you feel it? I believe it's trying to oppress you."

"Yes, Mary, it's really getting to me, and I agree it's targeting me more than anyone else in our home."

"Here's what I believe. Human spirits can be frightening, but you can make peace with them. Demons, however, take control of whatever and whoever they can. Demons are all about creating chaos, confusion and mayhem. People who are tormented by demons will have night terrors and often experience being touched."

"Absolutely. I've had many night terrors. I've also been touched, scratched and punched multiple times."

Connie came running over to us because she captured something fascinating on video.

"You guys have got to see this. I think we just captured an orb. Not only that, there's a face inside the orb, and it looks exactly like a skull."

Connie showed us the video and sure enough, I could see a face inside a rather large multi-colored orb. The face looked just like a skeleton with blacked-out eyes, a hole where the nose goes and I even saw a few teeth. It was incredibly detailed and quite unnerving.

I was feeling a little overwhelmed. What they captured in such a short amount of time was impressive. My brain was trying to find any kind of rational explanation for it, but I already knew the truth. My house is intensely haunted. Is it the house, though? Or is it me? I believe it's me, but I can't wait to hear what the ladies think. We even heard Indian chanting on another EVP. What I saw on the video and heard on the recorders was extraordinary. All the things I'd already seen, heard and felt were finally confirmed.

The investigation ended, and the ladies were packing up their equipment. Mary came over to tell me they wanted to have a short meeting with me before they left. I have a feeling they know what's inside my house. I felt excited, yet apprehensive. I don't know if I'm ready to hear the truth, but will I ever be? I believe there's power in knowledge, so I'm praying that's the case today.

I made coffee and had it all ready to go when they were finished. We sat down at the kitchen table with coffee and cookies.

I could feel my body tensing up the moment Mary began to speak.

"Julie, we believe there's a demon in your home who controls the human spirits here."

"Wow, nothing like jumping right in there, Mary!"

"It was a nice icebreaker, I thought."

The entire room erupted in laughter and it was exactly what I needed to help me relax a little. Jill was sitting next to me. She gently patted my arm and said, "Don't worry, we are here to help you. We have lots of experience chasing evil away."

I felt tears welling up in my eyes.

I believed her, but it still terrified me talking about a demon being here while still sitting inside my house.

"Jill, are we safe talking about the demonic entity while still inside the house? I mean, is it going to make things worse?"

"Julie, if you have a demon attached to you it doesn't matter where you talk about it. It can still hear you. We believe it's been with you since your childhood."

That just hit me like a brick.

"In all our years of investigating, this was by far the scariest case we have ever come across. It's the most significant infestation of darkness we've ever witnessed."

"I'm surprised you got all that in the short time you were here. I mean, are you sure? You didn't even examine your equipment before you came up with that conclusion. I guess part of me wants to be in denial. It's one thing to think it, but it's another when it's hitting you in the face."

Mary was the next to speak up, "Julie, we know this is hard, but you said it yourself, 'knowledge is power' and now is the time for you to get strong. I know you can do it. Truth is, you brought the spirits to you. You emit a light from within. You're like a magnet that attracts souls. You don't believe it yet, but you're incredibly gifted."

"Mary, I kept it at bay most of my life, so why now?"

"It's your awakening. A powerful turning point in your life. What does it all mean? It means you're going to be seeing a lot more spirits, dear."

I probably was born with abilities. I don't remember having any paranormal experiences as a child. However, I think I've blocked out a lot from my childhood. Even after my near-death, out-of-body experience, I successfully shut it down years ago.

Now is the time, and this is the place. This house is my awakening.

Janet, who had been sitting quietly sipping her coffee, spoke next.

"In most cases, investigators look at the history of the house itself. In your case, we couldn't rely on that because your house is too new. So, we had to look at the history of the land. My intuition makes me believe there was some kind of Indian curse placed on this land many, many years ago, and it's still going strong today."

"That's incredible. I don't think I've told you about my Indians and the many times they've come to me in my dreams. I've also found effigy mounds. Some are even behind Mary's house along the Willamette River. This leads me to wonder if these houses were built on sacred burial grounds."

This time Mary spoke up, "I've also wondered about that, but we still need to do more research. Aside from all that, we wanted you to know we believe the demon you saw in your television is the same demon that attached to you as a child. We would like to perform a cleanse of your house. We need a couple days to prepare because we need to find a masculine male medium to help push the stronger male spirits off your property. We need to find a few more Reiki masters to help cut the cords of low-level straggler spirits that we also know are present. More importantly, we will need to be in a State of Grace for this cleanse."

"What does 'State of Grace' mean?"

"I'm surprised you're asking me that, Julie, aren't you Catholic?"

"Well, I used to be. Now I consider myself a recovering Catholic."

"Mind if I ask why?"

"They abused me in Catholic school because I'm left-handed."

"Oh, I get it. You're the devil."

"That's pretty much what the nuns thought."

"Good to know. We should probably monitor you as well."

"Hilarious, Mary."

The more time I spent with her, the more I liked her. I love her sarcastic personality.

"One last thing before we go, Julie."

"Oh Lord, what now."

"Another side effect of being a medium is having PK abilities, or Psychokinesis. It's sometimes referred to as 'telekinesis' or mind over matter. It's the ability to move things or affect the property of things with the power of the mind. Of all the psychic abilities, PK is one of the rarest, and we believe you possess it."

"Is that why the lights in our house have randomly exploded?"

"Yes, we believe your PK abilities caused the items on the mantle to move around as well. Emotions and stress can affect your surroundings. Objects can move on their own, electronics can go on and off; you can even drain batteries."

"Jesus, that's a lot."

"We also think you may have created a poltergeist. People who have been through a lot of trauma can create a poltergeist without even knowing it."

"Hey, how about we save that for another day? My brain is overwhelmed. I'm afraid if I hear anymore weird things about myself, I might explode."

"Sorry Julie, we know this is a lot to take in. Let's table it for now. We'll be back in three days to cleanse. We'll have more information for you at that time. We also need you to prepare. We want you to be at your strongest and ready to take back control of your house."

"I'm ready, thanks to you wonderful ladies. I don't feel so alone anymore. I'm at a loss for words to express just how much I appreciate all of you."

"Julie, most of us are mediums, so trust me, we know."

"Mary, time for you to go home." *Wink, wink.*

"Love you too, Julie."

After everyone left, I was feeling overwhelmed, but also a little hopeful for the very first time. It's one thing to wonder if something demonic is residing in your home, but quite another when someone actually confirms it.

I pray God will give me the strength and the tools I need to conquer this.

34

I couldn't sleep at all last night. I'm so nervous about the cleanse today. I haven't told Jeff about it, either. It's better he doesn't know. Not better for him, better for me. It's been a little strained between us lately. Keeping the peace is important to quiet the activity. I didn't tell Stephanie because she's just a kid. She shouldn't have to deal with this.

How is this my life?

Mary showed up early to give me a little breakdown of what to expect before the rest of the ladies arrived. I wasn't at all prepared for the first thing she said.

"Julie, I've invited a demonologist to join us today. Her name is Stacy, and I know you'll like her. She's actually a lot like you. We didn't feel adequately prepared to deal with this powerful of a demon without her. Are you comfortable with me springing this on you?"

"Yes, I appreciate the fact that you're doing everything you can to help me. I trust you completely."

"Fantastic. I had a feeling you'd be cool. Ok, before everyone arrives, there are a few things we need to talk about. I want you to be strong and prepared to fight if you have to. Try not to be afraid, that only helps make the demon stronger. It's important to stand your ground. Be careful and smart about what you do, but be firm. We don't want this demon to stay attached to you. We caught another EVP I haven't shared with you yet. The demon acknowledged it's been with you throughout your life and it doesn't have any intention of leaving. This is very important. If you don't take control back of yourself as well as your space, you could lose it."

"Mary, I'm not feeling so afraid anymore. I was before you got here, but the fact that so many people are coming to help me means so much. I think I'm ready. This thing needs to go. By the way, do demons have names or . . .."

"Never ever say a demon's name out loud. Some demonologists will pull their name out during an exorcism, but we aren't skilled in that technique, so we play it safe and don't acknowledge it by name. I recommend you never say a demon's name out loud, ok?"

This is some intense shit.

"Ok, understood."

I'm clearly at a loss for words.

"Julie, one more thing before everyone shows up."

"Mary, I'm going to be exhausted by the time everyone gets here. Can't we just sit and have some tea while we wait?"

"Sorry, but no. We need to deal with all those mirrors in your house, especially the ones facing each other in your bathroom. This land created a vortex, which holds a lot of interdimensional energy. A vortex can be a portal, but a portal isn't always a vortex. We think the demon used the energy of the vortex to open up portals, then called human spirits through the mirrors to use against you, mainly to frighten you. The energy of fear and anger is what they feed on. It's how they gain their strength."

Mary told me we needed to close the portals one by one.

"We only have an hour, so we'd better get on it. I have a Saint Benedict medal on the end of a string with a crystal to use as a pendulum. The medal will rotate to show if there is a portal inside the space. The pendulum swings counter clockwise when it identifies an exit portal. The pendulum swings the opposite way, clockwise, for an open portal. Never, ever close an exit portal. You want to give the spirits a way out. We are going to close the entry portals."

It was interesting watching Mary work. She started in the kitchen and took tiny steps. It didn't take long for the pendulum to start swinging clockwise, indicating an open portal. The closer she got to a portal, the faster the pendulum swung. It was an incredible thing to witness.

Mary explained the process to me.

"I channel the energy through my body into the earth, up again through my feet, into my torso, along my arms and out through my hands. Then I state my intention to close the portal. When you see the pendulum completely stop, you know the portal has been closed."

"Mary, I'm in complete awe of you. I don't think I could ever do this."

"Julie, you are more powerful than you know. I'm showing you so you can continue to do this after we leave. Trust me, you're going to have to. Portals get opened all the time. This won't end today, this is going to be a lifelong battle, I'm sorry to tell you."

"I had a sneaky suspicion already."

Mary and her team suspected the coat closet was a satanic portal because of the dramatic raise in temperature when they came close to it.

"Julie, we need to say a prayer to close the satanic portal. I'm going to have you say it because it will help you gain more strength. Don't back down or show any weakness. Are you ready?"

No.

"Yes, I'm as ready as I'm ever going to be."

"Ok Julie, here's the prayer. Just take a few deep breaths, then read it out loud. Remember what I said about intention. Setting the intention is everything. Heartfelt prayer is the only way to effectively close satanic portals. Don't just say it, mean it."

Alright, here I go . . .

Father I confess my authority over Satan and all his host
in the name of Jesus Christ.
I renounce and destroy all satanic royal blood lines
from my ancestry,
I cut these blood lines off me in the name of Jesus.

Any doorways which I or my ancestors have opened
I now declare forever closed.
Thank you Jesus for closing all portals and gateways
the enemy would try to use against me and
your kingdom. Amen

When I was done reciting the prayer I felt so incredibly strong and confident. I had just called upon a power much greater than myself or any demon I will ever encounter . . . the mighty power of God. I feel empowered now to move forward and rid my home of the evil that has held me down for such a long time.

"Mary, that was incredible, I feel amazing."

"That's exactly what I was hoping for. When you gain confidence, there's no end to the wonderful things you can do. You're extremely gifted, you just haven't embraced it yet. I have a feeling your unique abilities and psychic powers are about to take off. You're finally starting to believe in yourself."

"Thank you, Mary. I know it's easier said than done, but I definitely need to try harder to have more confidence and strength within myself. I'm a work in progress but I feel my self-esteem is going to benefit in the long run."

"Julie, your spiritual journey has just begun. You need to stop listening to the garbage they fed you as a child. That doesn't have to be your reality any longer. You are stronger and more powerful than you think. You're the only one who can put it behind you. I will be here to help guide you all the way, but for right now we have another job. Any idea how to remove a mirror?"

"How about a sledgehammer?"

"Sounds like fun, but let's try a less messy way first."

We were lucky all we had to do was remove some hooks around the edge of the mirror. To our relief, it was easy to remove. As soon as we lifted the last mirror off the wall, the rest of Mary's team arrived. It surprised me how young Stacy looked. Never in a million years would I have ever pegged her for a demonologist. But, in all reality, what is a demonologist supposed to look like? Maybe a staunch priest? I was so glad she wasn't anything like that.

"Nice to meet you, Stacy. Welcome to my home. I hope it behaves for you today."

"I hope it doesn't. Don't worry, we are up for the fight. Shall we begin?"

I'm feeling like I've already run a marathon and Mary sensed it.

"Hey everyone, can we take a break and sit and chat for a moment before we do the cleanse? Julie and I have been hard at work closing portals and clearing out mirrors. We could both use a little break. Let's sit and have a spot of tea first."

I looked over at Stacy and she gave me a knowing glance. I felt comfortable with her the moment she walked into my home. I don't always trust people this fast, but there was something about her that put me at ease.

"Mary, I'd love to talk to Stacy first and get her take on what's going on here. Stacy, have you sensed anything yet?"

"I think whatever is here is intentionally hiding at the moment. Don't let that lull you into a false sense of security. Some of the worst experiences I've ever had, came after such a calm. From what Mary shared with me, there's no doubt in my mind you're dealing with a demon and probably have been for a really long time."

"Mary, did you tell Stacy I saw a horned figure in my television a while back?"

"Yes, but didn't it actually manifest outside of your television?"

"It sure did. When I walked back into the room it was standing directly in front of me. I couldn't move, I felt completely frozen."

Stacy shocked me a little with the intensity in her voice. We went from having a light conversation to all business.

"Demons are violent. Demons can also manifest in different forms. They want to pull as much fear out of you as they possibly can. They feed off your fear because it gives them more strength to use against you. Do not show fear. Ever!"

Easier said than done . . .

"During our cleanse today it might get intense, in fact I expect it to. Do your best to push the energy away from you. Stay in this world by planting your feet firmly on the ground. This will help you stay grounded here and not get drawn into the next realm. Demons take over the house, then they take over the person. If you see any scratches or bruises on your body, it's from something that was never human. It wants to possess your soul and we have every intention not to allow it."

I'm feeling overwhelmed again.

"Sorry everyone, but I don't think I can do this. I never asked for any of this, why is it happening to me? I don't know how to manage my abilities. *Abilities I never asked for.* Most of all, I don't know how not to be so afraid. Whatever is here is incredibly skilled at scaring the hell out of me."

I didn't realize I was on the verge of a panic attack, but I know Mary sensed it.

"Julie, stop. It's going to be alright. Take some deep breaths and try to relax."

Mary was superb at sensing when I was about to go off the rails. We hadn't even been friends long enough to have that kind of connection. It was like she knew exactly what I was thinking.

"I'm sorry everyone, I didn't mean to freak out. This is all so new to me. Part of me still doesn't want to believe this is happening."

Stacy walked over to me and calmly spoke in almost a whisper. It was very comforting.

"Julie, I need you to be strong and ready to face this thing head on. It's going to do everything in its power to stop you. We are here to support and guide you, but you are the only one who can drive this evil out of your home. Do you feel ready to do this now?"

"I wasn't before, but I am now. I didn't know how not to be afraid and its really making me mad that I've given this evil bastard power over me, and inadvertently allowed it to torture me ever since we moved here."

"That's good, take that anger and use it. Keep getting angry. Anger is exactly what you'll need to conquer your fears, so keep it going. I'm not trying to scare you, but if we don't finish this cleanse, it's going to get a whole lot worse. Take this information and turn yourself into a brave warrior. Don't worry, we will call upon God's angels to assist us, too."

I swallowed my last sip of tea, stood up and said, "Let's do this, ladies!"

I heard a warm chuckle as everyone stood up at the same time. I felt a peace come over me that surprised even me. It was only a moment ago that I was fighting off a panic attack. I'm feeling strangely calm, as if I already had some angels guiding and protecting me.

Before we began the cleanse, we placed holy crosses above the main entrance doors. One above the front door, one above the door leading into the garage and one above the sliding glass door in the back of the house. We also placed blessed Saint Benedict medals above all doors and in areas of activity around the house. The Saint Benedict medal is a source of protection against the devil. It's also a source of strength.

As we began the cleanse, I heard a strange noise that I didn't recognize. I asked Stacy if she'd ever heard anything like it before.

"Yes, unfortunately I have. There's a belief that demons tear through the atmosphere as they enter into our dimension. It makes a sound similar to paper tearing. I thought I heard paper tearing, is that what you heard?"

"Yes, I just hadn't figured out what it reminded me of yet, but you're right. It does sound like paper tearing in a strange way."

"There's definitely a demon here, and he knows what our intentions are. Stay strong."

Stacy grabbed my hand and squeezed it a bit, as if to say she was here to support me. The added strength it gave me was very much needed.

We did our best to ignore the bizarre sounds as we continued with the cleanse. The sounds were growing louder and louder. The demon was trying to distract us, but everyone did an outstanding job of not showing any weakness.

Even me.

Next, we placed holy water and blessed salt in every corner of each room. We buried the blessed medals in the four corners of the property outside to keep negative energy out. Then Stacy started speaking.

"I'm calling in the guardians of the four corners. East is for air,

South is for fire, West is for water, and North is for earth." Together we carried lit candles and sticks of burning sage.

"Julie, I use some unique elements during my cleanse. I'm pulling this from Wicca, and then we will later pray to Saint Michael. I feel strongly I need to hit this with everything I've got."

"I only know one religion, but I'd be open to learning about others. I'm definitely not closed off to the idea."

Mary chuckled, "Especially since you consider yourself a 'recovering' Catholic."

"Amen to that!"

"Ok girls, back to work. East is represented with sage. South is represented with a lit candle. West is blessed water. North is salt." Together we spread blessed salt around the entire perimeter of the house.

"Now we need to call upon a higher power and Julie, we need you to do this part."

Stacy handed me the prayer and as I took it, I noticed my hand was shaking. When I began speaking, I felt a sharp stab in my back and along my right side. I cried out in pain.

"Julie, don't stop, keep praying."

I gathered up every ounce of strength I had and continued . . .

Saint Michael the Archangel, defend us in battle.
Be our protection against the wickedness and snares of the devil.

I stopped praying because the entire house felt like it was shaking. My favorite crystal chandelier in the front entryway crashed to the floor and shattered.

"Keep Praying!" yelled Stacy. Only this time she sounded as if she were yelling at me from another room instead of standing right next to me. Everything felt so strange. The air felt like it was moving faster. When I looked at the other ladies in the room, it was like I was looking at them through a wavy mirror in a fun house. It was all very creepy. At that moment, I knew I was being affected by an evil entity who desperately wanted me to stop.

Then, out of the corner of my eye, I saw it. It's charging toward me from down the hallway. I looked straight at it, and the pure hatred and anger on its face was horrifying. It had gray leathery skin, just like I'd seen before, but no hair on its head and black holes where the eyes are supposed to be. I only saw one horn standing up on top of its head. I knew this was a different demon than the one I saw in the television.

The noise was growing so loud and it felt like a train was crashing through the house. I don't really know where my new found strength came from, but I prayed again. As soon as I recited the words, "thrust into hell Satan and all evil spirits who prowl the world seeking the ruin of souls," everything just stopped. It was almost too silent. I could feel a difference in the air almost immediately. When my prayer became more intense, determined and strong, I knew it was working.

I get it now. It really is all about intention. I believe for now the demon that attached to me is gone. If it ever comes back, *and I'm told it could,* I'm better prepared to handle it.

Mary said one last prayer before we closed the cleanse.

Lord, please send your army of warrior angels here to protect this home and everyone in it.
Please send any demons or negative entities straight back to hell. Bless and heal Julie and protect her from all evil.
Forgive any wickedness that took place on this property, including murder.
I now declare this land blessed, purified, cleansed and made holy before you.

35

There's physical pain and then there's emotional pain. For me personally, it's much easier to heal from physical pain. Emotional pain stays with you. In my case, it attracted a demon to me.

What really saved me was my faith in God and the power of prayer. That may sound strange since I adamantly speak out against the Catholic church. I think it's because I never blamed God for what those people did. Mainly the nuns, they were horrible to me. They beat me, tied me down, called me names, publicly humiliated me and treated me like I was evil. All for being left-handed. I wonder if the demon attached to me while I was being tormented in the basement at Saint Joe's. Makes sense, especially if demonic entities are attracted to trauma. I doubt I will ever get the justice I deserved for how horribly they treated me. But then again, Karma's a bitch.

I got beat with a paddle for vomiting in church. Our entire school attended an open casket funeral. I was in first grade and sat next to Sister Mary Goretti.

I never saw a dead guy before.

I will never get the image of that old man out of my head. Even though I was completely freaked out, I just sat there staring at him. It was like a train wreck . . . you want to look away, but you can't. After a while, I started feeling sick. I asked Sister Goretti if I could go to the bathroom, but she wouldn't let me. She slapped her boney hand across my face and told me, "If you don't sit there and behave yourself you're going to get the paddle in Mother Superior's office." What choice did I have? I leaned over the pew and threw up on her foot.

I guess that was my little piece of justice.

Why wouldn't I hate them? Why shouldn't I? I was an innocent child, it wasn't my fault I was left-handed. Why on earth would anyone think being born left-handed is all it takes to make a person evil? *So stupid.* I used to think anyone who was the slightest bit different was labeled as "evil" by the nuns. These were the monsters in my childhood who hid behind God to abuse us kids. They were the evil ones, not us.

My abuse lasted until I finally escaped in sixth grade.

Let's not forget about my abusive mother waiting for me at home. I refer to my childhood as an, "Experiment in terror." Aside from my faith, I believe I was gifted with some powerful spirit guides. I went from being abused in school to coming home to a mentally ill, narcissistic mother at home. Looking back, between my mother and the nuns, perhaps a demon wasn't the worst evil I've ever had to deal with.

Now that I know I'm the beacon for spiritual activity, what can I do to maintain peace and harmony in our home? The cleanse was intense and it took me more than a few days to recover. It really zapped my energy. Now that I'm feeling better, I need to do a few more things to maintain homeostasis at home. The first thing I need to do is take the advice of the investigators and get rid of that antique dresser that belonged to Jeff's grandfather. They got some evidence that something negative was attached to it, so it has to go. I'm hoping Mary has time to assist me with one more chore.

"Hey girl, have you recovered from my house, yet?"

"Well Julie, it wasn't the worst I've seen, but it was up there."

"Mary, I still need to get rid of that dresser. How should I destroy it?"

"I'm glad you called me. There are several schools of thought about this. Some believe you shouldn't destroy a haunted item. Some think the only way to dispose of it is to bury it or throw it in a body of water. If you had called Stacy, that's exactly what she would have told you to do. Personally, I feel that's giving the item too much power over yourself. I would just throw it in the dumpster, ask your spirit guides to release it to the power of God and allow him to disperse the negative energy."

"Mary, I like how you think. Since it's too big to bury, and I don't want to risk being disrespectful by throwing it in the river, do you know anyone who owns a truck? We have a cool dump nearby. Let's go throw it off the edge and watch it hit the bottom."

Mary didn't waste any time responding with excitement.

"My husband's work vehicle is a truck. I love throwing things over the rail and into the pit at the dump. I can go anytime you like. But what about Jeff? Will he mind if we destroy his family heirloom?"

"I'll figure out a way to tell Jeff later. I don't think he'll mind. He's not that fond of it, and he only took it because nobody else wanted it. Who knows, but I don't want this thing in my home one more day."

Mary and I loaded the dresser in the bed of her husband's work truck and drove it to the dump. Mary backed the truck as far as she could to the edge of the dump pit.

"Wow Julie, that's a long way down to the bottom. We picked a great day to come. The pit is completely empty! That's got to be at least forty feet down."

"More than that, I bet. I've never seen the pit this empty before. Must be our lucky day. Let's remember to say a prayer asking God to disperse the negative energy before we send this thing crashing back to hell."

"Wow Julie, you really have a way with words. How about the protection prayer? It's short and sweet, but it will get the job done. It's pretty powerful."

Mary pulled a card out of her pocket and handed it to me.

"You need to be the one to say it."

The Light of God surrounds me
The Love of God enfolds me

The Power of God protects me

We moved the dresser to the edge of the pit and let it fall. It exploded into a bunch of tiny pieces when it hit the ground. I saw a plume of solid blackness rising up from the wreckage, circled around me, then faded into the air.

I don't understand how spirits can attach to an object. The even bigger question in my mind is why? I guess things just aren't that important to me as they are to some people. That's probably because my mother was so into shopping and "material objects" were the only things that made her happy.

Well, temporarily happy.

If I hadn't experienced this myself, I never would have believed it.

36

Things have been calm lately, almost too calm. Maybe it's just me. I feel like I'm waiting for a bomb to go off. Even Jeff and I are getting along much better. He didn't seem to mind when I broke the news to him about his grandfather's dresser. *He even laughed a little about it.* Maybe things are looking up. Some weird things have been happening, but nothing too alarming. Just some little oddities that made me wonder, but not enough to really be able to say with certainty it's paranormal.

I broke my rib the other day. I'll admit, I'm a little clumsy and I shouldn't blame it on anything paranormal, but this felt strange. Summer is coming, which means time to hang flower baskets and plant annuals. I like to plant rows of impatiens and then fertilize the heck out of them until they grow almost as tall as me. It's possible with the right fertilizer. I also use it more often than the label recommends. Neighbors love to see my flower garden and some even stop to take photos. It gives me such a sense of pride, and it also makes our home look like a little country cottage. There's just something about flowers that brings me happiness and peace. I think my neighbors benefit from them as well.

I was standing on a stepladder so I could fertilize the hanging basket outside our front door. I had just reached up to pour the fertilizer into the basket when I felt a little like I was shoved from behind. I tried to get my balance back, but couldn't. It felt like slow motion when I slipped and landed hard on the top rail of the stepladder. I could feel something crack on the right side of my chest. I was sure I broke a rib. I got in to see my doctor later that day. He ordered an x-ray which confirmed I indeed had a fractured rib.

But, feeling like I'd been pushed wasn't the part that bothered me the most. That could be easily explained away. Perhaps I just lost my balance. I shouldn't blame everything on the paranormal. No, the part that bothered me the most was what happened after I got myself off the stepladder.

Something strange happened when I tried to open the front door. It felt as if someone was on the other side pushing back. I closed the door, thinking something must be blocking it, but no luck. It still felt like someone was on the other side trying to push me back. So, I closed it again, but this time I pushed it with more force. The door swung open so hard it left a dent in the wall. It was perplexing because I was the only one home at the time. I'm convinced something was keeping me from opening the door. But what? Little unexplainable odd things like this have become more commonplace. Strange, almost elusive phenomena that you just can't quite put your finger on. Weird enough to notice, but not scary enough to worry about, so you just brush it off.

Maybe that was the intention.

Later that same night, I thought I heard a man whistling a song I didn't recognize. However, I had just gone to the doctor and was given some pain meds for my cracked rib, so I blamed it on that. It sounded distant too, so I debunked it as possibly coming from someone outside. Deep down, though, I knew it wasn't coming from outside. This drives me even more crazy than the obvious, "scare the crap out of you" stuff that used to frequently occur.

Another weird thing that keeps happening . . . I keep waking up in the morning with my hair covering my face. I have long hair and there's enough to completely cover it, but I've never woken up before with all my hair pulled over my face. *It's so strange.* It wouldn't be so odd if it only happened one time, but this has happened every single day for the past two weeks. Again, it's not enough to alarm me or incite fear like before, but it's just so freaking odd.

One more example . . .

I keep seeing black spiders when I'm sitting on the right side of the couch in the family room. Every time in that same exact spot. I will be sitting there watching television when I think I see something move. When I look over, I see a huge black spider crawling up the armrest, coming within inches of my right arm. I freak out, jump up and run to the kitchen to grab a napkin to kill it with. *I really hate spiders.* By the time I come back, it's gone. Just completely vanished. Nobody else is seeing big black spiders, just me. And only in that location. This has happened at least ten times.

Wow, this just hit me, I just described a total of three strange new occurrences in my home. *Three.* Maybe it's just me, but I feel like this is some kind of synchronicity. For example, the witching hour is three in the morning. Also, the holy trinity is represented by the Father, the Son and the Holy Spirit. *Just another example of a set of three.* Demons mock the holy trinity by scratching in sets of three. The list goes on, but I wonder if there's some meaning to it all. I guess time will tell.

Even though it doesn't sound like much, these experiences were taking a toll and causing me to have a lot more anxiety. I was becoming more emotionally and physically drained. Most of the time, when things got weird in my home, I'd just jump in the car and drive away. I felt comfortable in my car until I was shown one day that I really wasn't safe there either.

Jeff had just arrived home from work. He was down the hall changing his clothes when I heard him call out to me.

"Julie, are you alright?"

"Yeah, I'm just sitting here watching TV. Why do you ask?"

"I just heard you yell out the word 'wow' as if you needed help."

I thought that was strange. I assured him if I needed help, "wow" wouldn't be the word I'd normally use.

Later that same evening we were on our way home from doing some shopping. I remembered the earlier incident and wanted to chat a little more about it. I couldn't remember what Jeff said I called out to him, so I asked him again to clarify what he heard me say.

"Jeff, earlier today when you heard me call out to you, what was it I said? Was it, 'wow' or 'oh shit?' I can't remember what you told me."

"All I heard you yell out was the word 'wow' and you said it like you were in pain and needed help."

"Oh, ok, I get it. Like it made you think I was in some kind of pancreas pain, or something?"

"Yes, that's exactly what I thought."

"Again, that's weird. First, I never yelled out anything to you and second, it's not the word I'd say in that instance. The strangest part is, I never yelled out to you at all. I believe you heard a spirit mimic my voice again."

Most likely a demon is what I was really thinking . . .

Before Jeff could respond I heard a creepy voice that sounded like it was coming from the car radio. It was a deep guttural laugh, and it came across more like, "huh-huh-huh" rather than, "ha-ha-ha." It also sounded like it was coming from far away. I hadn't even turned on the radio. How is that even possible? I couldn't believe it, but this time Jeff heard it, too. We drove down the street in silence, still trying to make sense out of what had just happened. The sun was fading behind our house as we drove closer to our destination.

Jeff broke the silence and said, "Maybe it was just the brake drum or the motor."

"Yeah, sure thing."

"Mr. Skeptic, I get so annoyed with you sometimes. What will it take for you to believe this shit is happening? Hell no, it wasn't the motor. It was a very distinctive mocking type of sinister scare-the-shit-out-of-you laughter."

When things like this happen to me, I normally tend to isolate and go deep inside myself. But tonight, there's nowhere left to go and I don't think there's much chance of figuring this out. My safe place is nowhere. Even my car isn't free from the paranormal, anymore. Maybe I'm just tired and imagining it. No, I know what I heard. Something came through my car radio, there's no other explanation.

But why?

The next day, at the same time, I had the most intense pancreas pain hit me completely out of nowhere. I fell off the couch and landed on the floor. It even surprised me when I found myself doubled over, holding onto my stomach, and the word "wow" came out of me. That was followed by, "oh shit." I had just repeated the same words that Jeff and I spoke about the night before on the way home from shopping. I will never forget the sinister laughter that came out of my car radio at the same time. I just repeated the same exact words, and even in the same order. *This is too damn weird.* Had I just been attacked? What new brand of sick premonition was this?

I wish I could say I had all the answers, but that would be a lie. All I can do is describe the strange events that took place and hope someday answers will come. When you're fighting something you can't see, it's a whole new level of fear. I guess that's the point. Entities, especially demonic entities, feed off fear.

I must be like a smorgasbord to them.

37

J eff and I are were fighting more again. Over stupid things, too. And each time we fought, the energy in the house only got worse. The fights escalated to unnecessary and ridiculous anger. Sometimes I literally felt like I wanted to kill him. I'm sure there were moments when Jeff felt the same way, too. Sometimes, even my thoughts didn't feel like they were truly my own. It's hard to explain and even tougher to understand. I felt like something was trying to manipulate me into getting angry. I wasn't feeling in control anymore. We were both being influenced in a pretty intense way, we just hadn't quite figured it all out yet. I guess I needed to go through more hell before I could put all the pieces together. It reminds me of some of the chaos that took place before I drove the demon out of our home. Had we not completely gotten rid of it? Or has it come back?

In my defense, nothing major had happened yet, just random, hard to explain weird and bizarre stuff. Besides, denial is a wonderful thing. But seriously, nothing happened that was drastic enough to be able to know for certain we were dealing with the demonic.

Until that one night . . .

Around 11:30 p.m. the fighting got so bad we had to get out of the house. This time it was different, though. For the first time since we moved in, we weren't trying to get away from each another. Somehow, almost magically, we understood that we were being influenced by something evil inside our home. We were saying horrible things we'd never, ever consider saying to one another. Cruel, awful words were coming out of my mouth that I regretted saying the minute I said them. I just wasn't in control any longer, and neither was Jeff. We knew the anger was building into something dangerous.

It was really a blessing how it came to us to just stop talking. Jeff put his finger up to his mouth in an effort to get me to stop talking and then he mouthed the words, "Let's get out of here." It was understood between us we had to flee. I threw on my slippers and we climbed inside Jeff's truck. Jeff was so panicked to get away, I could see his hand shaking as he put the key in the ignition. He quickly backed out of the garage and sped down our street. He just drove with nowhere to go. We didn't care, we had to get out of that house. I know that sounds a little dramatic, but for us it was that serious. We didn't speak to each other again until we were completely away from our neighborhood. Then the words came flooding out of both of us, but this time, the right words. Words of regret.

"Julie, I'm so very sorry for the things I said to you. I don't know what came over me. I didn't mean any of the crap I said to you."

"I know, me too. I'm just glad we got out of there when we did, before it was too late."

"Any thoughts on where to go?"

"How about you get on the freeway and keep going?"

We had nowhere to go, but this time I wasn't alone like I'd been in the past. Last time I freaked out and left our house, I didn't even bother putting my shoes on. At least I didn't have to worry about Stephanie. She was safe and spending the night at a girlfriend's house.

The longer we stayed away, the calmer we felt. After driving around for about an hour and a half, reality hit us and we knew we had no other choice but to return home. Jeff turned his truck around and headed for home while I silently prayed.

We were relieved to wake up the next day with no more incidents. It's so strange how one second things are bonkers, and then the next, calm as can be. It's like a mental game of cat and mouse. So many strange random things were happening. Nothing to completely freak me out, but enough to go what the fuck?

∾

We keep our garbage can in the garage. A couple nights after we fled the house, I walked out into the garage to throw some garbage away. As I took the first step into the garage, a strange reflection on the cement floor caught my eye. It looked as if a pair of eyes were looking up at me. I tightly closed my eyes, and when I opened them back up again, it was still there. Just the eyes, nothing else. Could this be just a case of matrixing? It was enough to make me wonder, but I really didn't think so. I know what I saw, and I saw a pair of eyes looking straight up at me. Total eye contact until I finally broke free and ran back inside the house. I call these things that randomly happen, "head shakers," but it wasn't even close to the terror that about to unfold.

So, this was weird. I started noticing my underwear was coming up missing when I did the laundry. I'd look all over for it and when I gave up looking, it would somehow magically appear. Sometimes I found it placed on top of the dryer, and other times it would be scattered randomly throughout the house. One afternoon I found my panties hanging off the chandelier over the dining room table. What new hell has befallen me, now? Do I have some creeper spirit in my house taunting me? I try to ignore most of the weird stuff, but this crosses a line.

Throughout all this, the most important thing I've learned is that fear can be dangerous. If you allow negative energy in it can have a negative effect, but what if you don't know you're allowing it in? It can also weaken you and make you more vulnerable to evil spirits. Maybe if I just don't show fear anymore, this thing will go away. *Personally, I think it would be easier to lose fifty pounds overnight.* This stuff really freaks me out sometimes. Evil entities feed off of fear, so I'm sure that's why they all love it here so much.

The activity was definitely revving back up, I just didn't want to acknowledge it. I was hearing more knocking coming from within the walls again, and banging sounds from the washer and dryer. I was hearing some strange sounds coming out of the utility room, so I decided to investigate. I had almost reached the end of the hallway when I saw a gigantic black mass growing to where it completely filled the end of the hallway from floor to ceiling. It wasn't a black shadow like I'd seen in the past, but more of a big black blob. It had the consistency of black nylon where you could kind of see-through it even though it wasn't entirely see-through. As it moved closer toward me, it blocked out the light coming in from the bedroom windows.

I tried to run, but I became instantly frozen as ice-cold air blew across the back of my neck. I saw the mass begin to change. It became more solid as it shrunk down to half its size. Then it morphed into the silhouette of a person. I could see it a man as it came closer toward me. He reached out to touch my shoulder as I stood there still frozen from the ice-cold air, then he quickly blew through me. I've never felt a spirit move through me like that before. I was freaking out and desperate to run, but I was still frozen. Just as fast as he disappeared, he reappeared and put his cold bony hands on my shoulders, trying to pull me down the hallway toward the coat closet.

All I could do was pray. I closed my eyes and recited my prayer to Saint Michael. It's my most powerful tool in my battle against evil. Sometimes it feels like my soul is battling the darkness. At the end of the prayer, I opened my eyes, and it was gone. The house had sunlight coming through the windows again, and the room eventually warmed back to normal. I was proud that I didn't run out of the house this time. I think I'm getting used to it, if that's even possible. I sat down with some tea to get the insides of me back to normal temperature. It froze me clear to the bone.

I got a break from the weirdness for an entire day. The following morning, I was in the family room about to vacuum the carpet when I thought I heard something that sounded like multiple voices coming from down the hall. As usual, I was all alone. It amazes me how most of the activity happens when I'm alone. Pisses me off, too. *Maybe that's the point.* I quietly walked toward the master bedroom at the end of the hall. As I got closer, the sound grew louder. It sounded like lots of people were talking, I'm hearing many different voices, and they were all speaking at the same time. When I got to the end of the hallway, I was surprised to see the bedroom door was closed. We never close this door. I stood in front of the door and listened as the voices grew angrier. I looked under the crack at the bottom of the door and I could see shadows moving back and forth across the room.

My hand trembled as I reached out to touch the door handle. I took a deep breath, gathered all my courage and quickly turned the doorknob. The door flung wide open and the sound abruptly ceased. Aside from the room feeling almost as freezing cold as yesterday, nothing else was there. No people, no noise, just silence. My intuition already knew what was going on.

The demon was back, and he brought his friends with him.

My first thought was, how do I tell Jeff about this? I really don't have a choice this time, he deserves to know. Jeff has been having a bit of bad luck lately. He was in another car accident recently, his third in less than four months. Jeff wasn't seriously hurt, just a few bumps and bruises, but his car was back in the body shop.

Since our insurance doesn't cover car rentals, I was acting as Jeff's temporary chauffeur until they repaired his car.

The phone rang, and I jumped. My nerves are getting more frazzled by the minute.

"Hey babe, what's up?"

"I just got a call from a client. I need you to pick me up ASAP and take me to one of our accounts. Apparently, there's a flood in the bathroom."

"Alright, I'm on my way."

I was more than happy to get away from the house for a while.

The flood turned out to be just a small leak.

I dropped Jeff off at his office, then drove back home. As I walked in the back door, I thought I heard a noise coming from the kitchen. Stephanie was still in school, so our house should have been empty. I was a little fearful someone had broken in. Not that fearful, though. Chances are it's probably just that annoying paranormal crap again.

I really could use a break.

I grabbed a baseball bat just in case I needed to protect myself from a human intruder. *Hey, you never know.* I slowly and quietly tip-toed to the kitchen, growing more and more anxious the closer I got. To my amazement, when I came around the corner, I saw Jeff standing there leaning on the counter next to the sink with his back turned toward me. But, how is that even possible? I had just dropped him off at his office less than twenty minutes ago. Even if Jeff had access to a car, there's no way he could have beat me home. Against my better judgment, I called out to him. I waited for Jeff to turn around and say something to me, but he never responded.

I sensed I was in more danger than I realized and decided I'd better get the hell out of there. I quickly backed out of the kitchen and fled. I didn't know what was in my house, but I knew it wasn't Jeff. I've never shared this story with anyone, until now. I stayed away from the house all day long until it was time to pick Jeff up from work. Luckily, Stephanie would be busy with school activities until dinnertime. Whatever it was, it wasn't there when we got home.

Thank God.

I never found out for sure what it was standing at the kitchen sink that day, but my intuition tells me I most likely saw Jeff's doppelganger. I did some research at the library, but nothing conclusive came up other than doppelganger. It looked exactly like Jeff from behind. I'm also wondering if this is the thing that's been shape shifting into our likeness and mimicking our voices. I'm really glad it never turned around. I've seen plenty of terrifying looking faces, even some gross decomposing ones, and I wasn't in the mood to see another. You just can't un-see this stuff once it's inside your head.

38

I was hoping to wait until the perfect moment to tell Jeff, but I've never been very good at that sort of thing. I have no impulse control. Aside from all that, I was feeling incredibly stressed and needed someone to talk to. Besides, he's a big boy, he can handle it. He also has a right to know. If I was expecting support, I was sorely mistaken. Even I was a little surprised at his response.

"Oh sure, you really expect me to believe that bullshit? What's really going on here? I'm so fed up with this garbage. I'm not buying into your nutty delusions any longer. You're getting crazier by the minute. Maybe you need a psychiatrist. I never experienced anything like this until I married you. If I never hear the word, 'paranormal' again it will be too soon."

I didn't know how to respond to Jeff, so I just turned and walked away. My life was becoming a lonely, stressful existence. I was beginning to feel depressed and that's a dangerous place for me to be.

Even though Jeff and I had that one night of unity when we fled the house together, we were still growing apart. I was so incredibly hurt by what he said. I definitely won't be turning to him for support anymore. I was getting depressed. My anxiety had also ramped up. I was experiencing two to three panic attacks a day. I was becoming suicidal. I decided everyone would be better off without me since this was all my fault, anyway. I call it *stinkin' thinkin'* today, but when you're in the middle of all that stress, with some PTSD thrown in, you're not thinking straight. It seemed perfectly logical to me. I also wonder if I was being negatively influenced by something demonic. As I grew more and more depressed, I became more intent on taking my life. I blamed myself for all the paranormal activity and decided to spare my family from having to deal with it. I'm no stranger to suicide. I've lost friends, and even a close family member to suicide. I even attempted it once, many years ago. I'm not sure how serious I was. Now that I look back on it, I think it was more than anything else a cry for help. I cut my wrist. I still have the scar to remind me. I was glad I hadn't succeeded, but now those old thoughts are taking over. I've heard suicide referred to as, "A permanent solution to a temporary problem." But today those, "I'm not good enough" thoughts or, "Everyone would be better off without me" thoughts are becoming more and more impossible to shake.

I laid down on the couch to contemplate how I'd do it this time. I didn't realize I was slowly drifting off to sleep. Off in the distance I see a beautiful young girl slowly walking toward me. She was wearing a flowing white gown, her long black hair almost covering the right side of her face. I heard a voice off in the distance telling me not to worry. I was asleep, but having a very real spirit visitation. My intuition reassured me I had nothing to fear, so there was no need to wake myself up.

She came closer to me, pulled her long black hair far enough away to reveal deep burn marks on the right side of her neck. Instinctively, I knew she had taken her own life by hanging herself. She leaned over me and whispered, "It's going to be ok. You're going to be alright. Please trust what I'm telling you. Suicide is not the answer. I'm here to save you. By saving you I get to save myself and share my story."

It was strange how she could read my mind. I formed a question in my head, but before I could say it out loud, she answered it.

"No, it wasn't worth it, not at all. If I had the choice to do it again, I'd never choose suicide."

I had one last question for her.

"Yes, Jeff was being influenced by something evil to say those terrible things to you. Forgive him, it's not his fault. He's being manipulated by a dangerous evil who's only mission is to possess your soul. Don't allow it, by taking your own life. You'd only be giving in to evil. Fight hard, you can do this. Life is too precious not to."

When I looked up, she was gone. I woke from this incredible dream feeling a renewed sense of worth. Now I know a dark entity was responsible for putting all those negative thoughts in my head. It's drawing energy from me and leaving me with thoughts of hopelessness and despair. How did I not realize this before? It wanted to make me vulnerable, so it could eventually claim my soul. Demonic entities will bide their time until they know you're at your weakest.

Well, not this soul, you filthy demon. I have a prior commitment to God.

I'm taking my power back.

~

It's one thing to say you're taking your power back, but another to actually do it. I was still being physically attacked and mentally tormented. The next few days would be a turning point for me, but I still had to go through more hell to get there.

I was contemplating what to do next, when the phone rang. Not my cell phone, the one in the kitchen. We hadn't removed it yet. It's still not plugged in, so how the hell can it possibly ring? Why hadn't I removed that darn phone, yet? Stupid reason. It's because it would leave a hole in the wall. I nervously picked up the phone and held it to my ear. All I could hear was static. I was pulling the phone away to hang it back up when I heard a loud growl. I dropped the phone on the floor and screamed. I really need to get rid of that phone. We only kept it to lower our cable bill. I'd rather pay more money, then have to keep dealing with this. Who am I fooling? It could just call my cell phone, instead.

I calmed myself down and picked the phone up off the floor and placed it back on the receiver. I had only taken a few steps out of the kitchen when I felt a tingling sensation on my left leg. It felt like multiple cob webs were covering my leg and tightening around my knee. I've never felt anything like this before. I knew I was being tortured by the demon who just called, even though I didn't want to admit it. In a matter of seconds, my leg went from tingling to feeling like it was on fire. It felt as if I was being stung by an entire hive of angry bees, all at the same time. I was in terrible pain, but I couldn't move. This time I wasn't frozen in fear, I was on fire and paralyzed. It was one of the worst experiences I've ever had in this house. It's a terrifying feeling when you need to run for your life, but you can't because you're completely paralyzed.

As I struggled to break free, I had a vision. I'm pretty sure it was the demon who gave me this vision. It was like I really went back in time to watch myself relive a terrible moment in my childhood. The only choice I had was to stand there and watch since I was being completely controlled by a monster. The vision began when I was nine years old playing tag at my friend Sandy's house down the street. I was running across their front yard when I ran over a beehive in the ground. Who knew bees could build hives in the ground? I certainly didn't. Hundreds of bees instantly came swarming up from the ground. I ran as fast as I could to get away from them, but they were aggressive and chased me all the way home. They flew up my pant legs and got stuck in my hair after stinging me multiple times in the head. Before the vision ended, something else happened. Off in the distance I saw it. The demon who plagued my childhood was standing on the sidewalk across the street from my house. He was watching me in sheer delight as I cried out in pain.

Sick bastard, I was just a little girl.

When the vision ended and I could move again, I reached down to feel my leg. Huge welts had developed all around my knee. When it got to the point when the pain was intolerable, everything just stopped. The welts on my leg directly above my knee spelled out the words, "help me." I was completely freaked out but at least I wasn't in excruciating pain anymore. No doubt in my mind, the demon who put the vision in my head was the same demon standing across the street watching me suffer when I was just a child. Like I said, sick bastard.

The room went from being on fire to instantly frozen. I felt frigid breath blowing across the back of my neck. *This is becoming all too famil-iar.* I slowly turned around, and not at all surprised, nothing was there. I hear the words, "I'm dead, I want you to join me" breathed into my left ear. Every muscle in my body tensed up. I try to turn *to do my usual thing and run* when I heard what sounded like a witch's cackle. Between the frigid cold air in the room and my tensed-up muscles, there's no way I'm going anywhere. It was an incredibly helpless feel-ing. This time, sheer terror rendered me paralyzed. I was at the mercy of something evil, holding me against my will. How can I fight some-thing I can't even see?

The moment of pure panic had arrived, but instead of freaking out, I got mad. No more, enough is enough. I have finally found my inner strength. I yelled at this thing at the top of my lungs to get the hell out of my house. I meant it. I was so furious, I even surprised myself.

I began to pray . . .

I hadn't even made a conscious decision to pray. Well, not yet anyway. I was saying a prayer out loud, but it didn't feel like it was me who was speaking it.

I've never had anything like this happen to me before.

Someone, *I didn't know who*, literally put words in my mouth, and it was working. I wasn't in control of what was happening, yet I felt safe and powerful. My intention was to conquer this evil entity once and for all. I sensed I was getting some divine help from the good guys on the other side, which made me feel even more determined.

Seconds later, something incredible happened. It arrived with a familiar warm glow emanating from all four corners of the room. Warmth quickly replaced the cold and spread throughout the entire house. I heard a rustling sound, and then I thought I saw wings begin-ning to appear. I couldn't see the angel straight on, but I could see the shadow on the wall of wings as they slowly spread out. The wings were massive. My prayers became much more intense as I completely gave up control to this higher power. I felt wonderfully comforted as I continued to be surrounded by the most amazing and loving warmth. A calmness came over me as my angel and I conquered the evil being so hell bent on my destruction.

At that moment it became clear. I was protected by angels and everything was going to be alright. *This is another story I kept to myself until now.* Who would believe me? I really don't care anymore. All that mattered to me was knowing the truth. I'm really not alone. I have some of the strongest, most powerful help from the other side. I don't have to be afraid anymore because I know I have warrior angels watching over me.

I'm going to always attract spirits, both good and bad, but today I'm more confident than ever before. I now truly believe I can handle anything. For the first time in forever, I know I have the power within me to fight off even the most powerful demons if I have to. Today was a real turning point for me. Today, I took my power back. I'm ready to stand up against any evil that dares to dwell within our walls and create havoc in our lives. My life changed in a moment's time. I accept my new mission. I'm ready to fight these evil entities. It has to come from me. I guess somewhere deep down I always knew. But today I feel more prepared than ever before. I'm stronger than any demon, especially when I have angels on my side. It's such a great feeling to know I'm not alone. I will always remember *and treasure* the moment my angel came to save me. I'm honored they chose me to fight in the battle between good and evil.

39

"Julie! Listen to me! Negative energy from the nearby graveyard has opened a very dark portal. You think you've taken your power back, but it's not enough. You must show them you're in control. *Intention is the key.* You must set boundaries in a way that is foreign to you, and be forceful. Most important, you mustn't show fear. Fear opens the door for them to come back in. If you don't do what I'm telling you, they will destroy you and everyone you care about. Never, ever show fear. You can do this. You're so much more powerful than you will ever know. Time to wake up and get to work."

I woke up soaking wet. Whenever I had a spirit visit me in my dreams, I always woke up the same way. I had many spirit visits in my sleep, mostly from my Grandma Eva, but tonight, I just had my very first visitation from my other grandma. Her name was Clarice. She was my grandma on my mother's side. I barely knew her. Not because she lived far away, she lived in the same town as me, just a ten-minute drive from my home. My mother and Clarice didn't get along, so I was never allowed to spend time any with her. She seemed nice enough to me.

I decided I wanted to get to know her when I turned sixteen. I used to sneak out to go visit her and my Grandfather Buck at their home. Unfortunately, a month after I started visiting her, she was diagnosed with Alzheimer's disease. Sadly, within a few short months, Clarice forgot who I was. Eventually the family moved her into a nursing home because she forgot who her husband was, too. She made a lot of 911 calls, claiming there was an intruder in her home. I bet that was tough on her husband, but terrifying for Clarice.

Every day after work I'd visit her at the nursing home, but it wasn't the same. When it was time for me to leave, she always said, "Nice to meet you, Shirley." Every single time she said those same exact words to me. Except for tonight. Tonight, she told me she loved me and actually called me by my real name. It was a wonderful visit from my other spirit grandma.

I've also been told that psychic abilities are passed down from mother to daughter. If this is true, I believe my abilities came from Clarice. I've heard some things about her and I know my mother has some clairvoyant abilities. It's a shame I will never know for sure. Clarice died before I could talk to her about it.

Clarice gave me some valuable advice, and my intuition tells me it came from personal experience. I'm not sure how she knew, but she also told me, "the spirit of the shaman has cursed the forest. So much disrespect of their effigy mounds, it woke an elemental to protect their sacred land." Elementals are the protectors of the forest. I wonder if Clarice learned this in the afterlife. Or, perhaps she already knew.

My Indian spirits were guardians of the effigy mounds. I need to find a shaman to help me make peace with the land. I didn't even procrastinate like I normally do. This was something long overdue and I genuinely wanted to show respect.

The first thing I did was to appease the elemental spirits by planting a tree at the entrance to the forest. I talked the city into allocating some funds to clean up the old abandoned cemetery and replace all the broken headstones. I needed to do everything I could think of to calm the spirits and show some honor for this sacred area. The city was more than agreeable, which really helped.

My next move was to call in an experienced shaman who could perform a healing ritual along with an offering to honor their ancestors. We burned some candles and made an offering of tobacco while asking the spirits to help us heal the land. We set an intention for peace. Long overdue peace. It was the most beautiful ceremony I'd ever witnessed. The shaman was incredibly knowledgeable about the land. He told me the effigy mounds by the river, the cemetery and my house formed a perfect triangle. I found that fascinating. I'm not sure what it means, but I believe it has some significance. Together with the Shaman and the Indian spirits, we were able to make peace with the land.

Finally, after all these years.

I was honored to help my Indians heal the land so people can finally live here in peace. Especially for the Indian spirits who still walk this land. I'm feeling great I could help make amends for the horrible things my ancestors did during the Puget Sound War.

This will *hopefully* bring peace to the Indian spirits at the effigy mounds, heal the cemetery, and calm the spirits who are still seeking amends from the war.

I had so many thoughts racing through my mind as I walked out of the forest. Something I hadn't thought about before stopped me dead in my tracks. It was Clarice's connection to the Indians. Interesting little tidbit, Clarice's last name was Brannan. The name of the man in Washington State who killed Indians out of revenge for the killing of his family was also Clarice's ancestor. Clarice came to help me make peace for the evil her ancestors did all those years ago. So strange how it's all connected. If it hadn't been for this house and this journey, I never would have known about my Washington ancestors and what went on there. I'm honored I could help put it all to rest.

I was feeling incredibly uplifted when I returned home. That didn't last for very long. I walked in the back door and took only a couple steps inside the house when I felt those cold bony fingers wrap around my neck. I was in no mood and feeling even more empowered than ever before. I yelled at the dark entity to back off. It's freezing cold, creepy fingers intensified the pressure around my neck to the point where I could barely breathe.

It's hard to explain what it feels like when the paranormal physically touches you. It's usually cold, but occasionally, I've also felt heat. I would rather feel cold than hot. The heat feels like it's coming straight out of the bowels of hell. It's a different heat than anything I've ever experienced before. For me, it's more mentally disturbing than anything else. To know that something *not of this world* is standing right next to me and worse, touching me kind of really freaks me out. I've never grown accustomed to it, and I probably never will.

I had no other choice but to reach out for help, so I prayed. I heard this evil thing speak in a language I've never heard before. I couldn't understand a word until it said, "Your God can't help you."

It spoke those words in very clear English.

I was terrified, but I knew I couldn't risk showing any fear. All my efforts could backfire, and then I'd be in even more danger. Eventually, my prayers worked. *Prayer always works.* I saw a bright flash of light hit the left side of this thing and in another instant, it was gone.

The best way to deal with the demonic . . . don't let it gain strength by feeding off your fear. That's why they try to look as scary as possible. They feed off the fear they create.

Trust me, I've seen some shit.

Demons can be unbelievably terrifying. One time the demon disguised itself as an angelic being of light to lure me in. It quickly turned into a half-human, half goat-like beast. The face looked human but with greenish-gray colored snakeskin and blood red glowing eyes. Long hair covered the lower half of the body and it had hooves instead of feet. I have to remind myself they only do this to incite fear. They put on a masquerade of deception. One time it appeared as a half roaring lion, half serpent. All meant to inflict fear upon its intended victim, only to strengthen itself.

Religious texts say that demons are attracted to human violence and desperation. Since I was abused as a child, both at home and at school, I believe it's what attracted the demon to me. I also wonder if a demon influenced my previous attempt to commit suicide. My intuition tells me it did.

Even though I was successful at expelling a demonic entity, I was still sensing negative energy in the house. It was manifesting primarily as a chaotic feeling. The next morning, I woke to the sound of birds chirping in our front yard. I opened the blinds to find over fifty crows and ravens gathering on our lawn. I've never seen anything like it, and I knew this was related to something evil. I've learned that crows and ravens are considered a symbol for evil. Not to call the birds themselves evil, just a symbol. In spirituality, if a raven appears to you, it's believed something positive or negative is about to change your life. I'm not sure if I believe that or not, but I find it odd there's so many birds on my front lawn. Considering everything else that's going on around here, I can only assume it's negative.

Aside from the obvious demonic activity that feels even more dark and taunting, I'm also sensing some more poltergeist activity. I've heard poltergeists are one of the most dangerous types of spirit a person can encounter. They cause items to fly off walls and are strong enough to kill. A poltergeist is created by a living person who's experienced intense emotional distress. I was lucky enough to have it all. Poltergeists, spirits and demonic entities.

My own personal trifecta.

After all that's happened, I'm convinced I had abilities long before my near-death experience. Maybe that evil thing that attached to me as a child is still trying to possess me. Perhaps it tricked me into believing I had gotten rid of it. I think the out-of-body experience brought me closer to the veil, but only intensified what was already there.

I nearly died two separate times from illness. Once when I was only two, and the next when I was fifteen. Maybe I was supposed to die and didn't. It drew something to me, perhaps death itself. Is there an angel of death? I feel it's much bigger than that.

I used to discount these ideas until I remembered something a priest once told me.

Yes, a priest.

"Julie, you need to reclaim your desire to stay on this earth."

I thought it was an odd thing to say at the time, and until recently I hadn't given it much consideration. However, when I combine it all together, all those desperate and depressed moments in my life, I realize I probably made myself vulnerable to the other side. Today, I reclaim my desire to remain on this earth through the good and the bad. Hopefully that will keep death at bay for a while longer.

Now that I've reclaimed my place in the world, I need to go get my house back once and for all. I finally broke through my fear, not to say nothing scares me anymore, but it wasn't that long ago when I was afraid of everything.

I've learned so much about the paranormal world and I feel ready to fight. I need to be the one to cast these negative energies out of my home.

Most of all, I need to set the intention and mean it. I need to do this right now before I lose my nerve. I took a deep breath, then said a prayer asking for strength.

There were so many words inside my head I was going to use, but what came out instead were the most powerful five words I've ever said.

"I'm done being a victim."

Suddenly I felt all the anger from being victimized my entire life rise to the surface. Abused by my mother, the Catholic school I went to, let's not forget my abusive ex-husband. I went back in time *in my mind,* remembering when I was brutally raped in college. I thought about the burned-out nurse who yelled at me to relax so they could examine me.

All those times I got no justice came out in one enormous bubble of rage.

I felt my anger intensifying.

"Get the hell out of my house."

Words can have a lot of power. It's not the amount of words you say, it's the intention behind them. I'm no longer feeling like a victim. Even so, I still need some extra muscle with this one. I called upon my strongest warrior, Saint Michael.

Saint Michael is an archangel and the leader in God's army of angels. He's considered a champion of justice, a healer of the sick and guardian of the church. In art, Saint Michael is often shown vanquishing Satan in the form of a dragon. He is honored in Christian tradition, but also among the Jews and Muslims.

That's why the angel who comes to my rescue the most is Saint

Michael. He's the main one I call out to. I'm not strong enough to handle demonic energies all by myself. I smudged with white sage until the air was thick with smoke. I'm no longer feeling vulnerable to the spirit world or any other aspect of my life.

Now it's time to reach out to my warrior.

Saint Michael, the Archangel,
defend us in battle.
Be our protection against the wickedness and snares of the devil;
May God rebuke him, we humbly pray;
And do thou, O Prince of the Heavenly Host,
by the power of God,
thrust into hell Satan and all evil spirits
who wander through the world for the ruin of souls.

When the smoke cleared the house felt brighter than it ever had before. It had a lightness to it. It felt peaceful for the first time since we moved here. Saint Michael and I are truly a force against evil. Nothing will ever hurt me or my family again.

40

I heard a knock at the door the moment I completed the cleanse. I jumped so high and my heart began to race. I had to calm myself down because I was nearly frozen in fear. What was I just saying about fear? I can't show it, that's what. *Come on, Julie, pull yourself together.*

I knew what this was because I'd been warned not to answer the door if I heard a knock. This was the demon. Evil was making one last attempt to get back in. I quietly approached the door so I could peek through the shears that ran along the right side. *Just in case I was wrong, and it was a neighbor.* No one was there, just as I suspected.

Before the cleanse, I opened a window for the demon to leave, but kept all the other windows and doors shut. I went to close the window, and I found another coin sitting on the windowsill. I took this as a clear sign the cleanse worked and the demon had left. Hopefully this time, it will stay gone.

The phenomenon of things falling or materializing out of thin air is called, "apportation." It's best described by Wikipedia as, "The ability to undergo materialization, disappearance or teleportation of an object." I've never heard of this, but then again, I never had coins appear out of thin air before, either. I've heard it's pretty rare. Coins are also a death reference. Many years ago, people used to place coins on the eyes of the deceased to help them gain access to heaven.

I took extra precaution and spread blessed salt around the perimeter of the house, just for some added protection. So far there has been no more knocking on doors or walls, no more disgusting smells and no more frightening activity. Well, nothing I would consider demonic, anyway. I still have plenty of spirit activity, but that's not nearly as terrifying. I'm pretty convinced the demon is gone.

Even though I'm relieved to have finally rid the house of evil, I still get plenty of strange activity. The following morning, I woke to a group of four or five spirits circled around me. I even felt a hand touching my shoulder nudging me awake. They spoke these words in unison, "Help is where we are."

I had a perplexed look on my face when one of the two females corrected the message and replied, "Help us, where are we?"

Then she told me the last thing they remembered was being in a car accident on the other side of our fence. There's a busy street that runs along the back side of our homes. I remembered right before we moved here, there was a fatal car accident on that road. The sad part was, they were all high school aged kids. Across the street is the local high school. I didn't know so many people had died. Sometimes, when people die suddenly or violently, they can get stuck here because they don't know they're dead. I didn't know what to do, I've never done anything like this before. I haven't read anything or been taught how to guide spirits into the light. However, it didn't matter because I felt I was guided to help these spirits. I envisioned the light and the rest came quite naturally. Everything magically fell into place.

After I envisioned a bright white light, I asked them to step into it. I said a prayer, then set an intention to help them cross over.

"Our father who art in heaven hallowed be thy name . . .
it's ok to let go of the human life you lived.
Go into the light and find peace.
God's unconditional love and forgiveness waits for you
inside the light."

Then I envisioned the light growing bigger and tried to give the spirits incentive to go.

"Go into the light now. Can you feel the love inside the light?"

I was sensing some hesitation, so I called upon Saint Michael to help me guide them into the afterlife. Once Saint Michael got involved, it only took a few seconds before I knew it was working. Finally, one by one, they faded into the light. It was the most incredible thing I've ever seen. I've helped many souls pass into the light since, but the first time was the most rewarding.

I've seen many spirits. I can't call spirits to me, I just randomly see them as they come and go. Most of the time they are passing through and don't want to interact. Sometimes they need my help to cross over. Whatever they need, I do what I can. It's always such a rewarding feeling when I'm able to help a lost spirit cross over. Occasionally, I will get a response such as, "I will go," or "I'm going home," but most of the time I just feel the energy lighten. When everything calms down and I'm able to feel more relaxed is when I know the spirit has moved on.

I don't believe there are very many earthbound, wandering or lost spirits. I believe demons can mimic and trick us into believing there are lost souls. Spirits can return from the afterlife for brief visits. There are also those who have unfinished business or don't know they have died. Some soldiers who died quickly might think they are still fighting the war. Then there are those who are afraid of what awaits them on the other side. Prisons and jails are high on the list of haunted places.

About those spirits who still have unfinished business . . . sometimes they can't rest until they've told their story or helped solve their murder. Some are here to help us learn to change the path of our own future. Some of their stories will remind us of how far we've come, but also how far we still have left to go.

There's so much more to this world than most people realize. If I hadn't experienced these things myself, or seen what I've seen, I probably wouldn't believe it, either. Everywhere I look there's magic in the world. It feels strange when I think it but, I already know things most people have to die first to learn.

41

Ever been waited on by a ghost? A bartender who didn't really exist or a nurse who was actually an angel? I've had so many terrifying experiences with the paranormal, but also a few incredible ones.

Anything is possible.

I saw a ghost on the street a few weeks ago when I was exiting the post office parking lot. I was being careful to check for pedestrians before pulling out onto the main street. Lots of people walk on the sidewalk in this area, so it's important to watch out for them. First, I looked to my left and when I looked over to my right, I saw him.

Well, the first thing I saw was just a poof of gray hair slowing rising above the back side of the apartment sign. Before I could look away, he jumped up from behind the sign with a big grin on his face. He looked directly into my eyes. He was very tall and thin, almost lanky looking. The strangest thing about him *at the time* was the fact that he was wearing overalls and a flannel shirt on a hot summer afternoon. I had no idea he was a spirit.

That was about to change.

Then he did something that really rattled me. I sat there in total bewilderment as he ran clear through the front end of my car. When he got to the other side, he turned around and looked back at me, nearly doubling over with laughter. He seemed like a jolly prankster type of spirit, just out having a little fun. I wasn't afraid of him at all, just a little stunned. He smiled and winked at me before he disappeared.

I just sat there for a moment trying to make sense out of what I just saw, but before long I was laughing, too. Sometimes it's nearly impossible to wrap my head around some of the strange things that just randomly happen to me. I didn't sit there for long, a car pulled up and honked at me to get out of their way.

Another time I was driving down a winding road called, "Indian School Road." It's a fun drive and there's an old Indian cemetery along the side of the road. I use it often because it's rarely traveled and I can avoid the busy main streets. I was driving down the road when I drove past a man on a bike. He was riding directly across from the Indian cemetery. It wasn't anything that out of the ordinary. It was just a guy wearing a suit riding a bike. The weird part about it was, it looked like something you'd see in an old silent film, and the bike looked like something out of the 1800's. I looked in my rearview mirror after I drove past him, and *even to my surprise* he wasn't there anymore. He had completely disappeared. It's moments like this when I know for certain I just saw another spirit.

I never used to see spirits out on the street, and certainly not this solid. This next experience happened recently, within the last couple weeks. I was on my way to a doctor appointment. I was stopped at a stoplight on one of the busiest streets in town. While I sat waiting for the light to turn green, I watched a woman as she walked across the street inside the crosswalk. I remember thinking, she'd better hurry and get across the street because the light was about to turn green. A few seconds later, the light turned green and the car next to me drove through the intersection, heading right for her. I was certain they were going to hit and kill this woman. I practically laid on my horn and frantically waved my arms, trying to get their attention. *They must have thought I was nuts.* In my defense, she looked real. That is, until the car drove through her. I was in such a state of disbelief, I don't remember if she disappeared after that or not.

At the same intersection, about a week later, I was waiting at a red light. I heard four tapping sounds on my side window. It was so alarming I jumped and almost hit my head. When I got the nerve to finally look to my left, nobody was there. Scared the crap out of me. I wonder if it was the same ghost that was crossing the street the week before.

Just so freaking bizarre.

I'd much rather see a spirit than hear a disembodied voice. The first time I heard a voice coming from out of nowhere? All I can say is it completely freaked me out. It's really hard to explain to people who've never experienced it. Imagine you're sitting alone in your home and out of nowhere you hear a voice. Knowing it's coming from someone who isn't part of this world anymore, I promise you, it's unnerving. I still get goosebumps when I hear a disembodied voice.

There's nothing quite like having a ghost whisper in your ear or worse, growl in your ear. There's a beautiful historic theater in our town called, "The Elsinore" theater. It was built in 1926 for silent films and vaudeville shows. It was heralded as the largest and most lavish theater between Portland and San Francisco.

Jeff and I had gone to see a comedy show there a couple years ago. We parked the car about a block away from the theater. As we walked to the theater, I could feel myself growing angrier with each step. I didn't know what was happening, but I knew the anger wasn't coming from me. I was excited to see a comedy show, and I had no reason to be angry. Yet, my anger was building to where I was so mad, I nearly bit Jeff's head off. He looked at me like I'd lost my mind when I told him, "I'm going upstairs to check out the balcony. Do not follow me."

Where did this anger come from? I had no clue at the time, but if I knew then what I know now, I would have gotten myself the hell out of there. Jeff was pretty angry at me by now, so he was probably relieved to get away from me. He walked across the theater to purchase a much-needed beer. I felt like words were being placed inside my mind. It felt like someone was trying to help me. The information felt like it was being downloaded into my brain.

"Julie, run! Turn around and get yourself right back down those steps. DO NOT go into the balcony. Run out of the building as fast as you can and never come back."

I completely ignored the message as being ridiculous and continued up the stairs until I reached the balcony. It's been a long time since I was in this theater. I'd forgotten how beautifully ornate the Elsinore is. It's by far the most beautiful theater I've ever seen. There's not a single thing to fear. I've spent plenty of time here. *I'm just being ridiculous and letting my imagination run wild.* My friends and I saw lots of movies here. We used to sit on the edge of the balcony and throw popcorn on our friends below.

I didn't know it, but I was being lured to the balcony by a sinister, unseen force. The voice inside my head wasn't warning me anymore, either. Now it was telling me to jump. As I stepped inside the balcony, I could feel pressure on my shoulders as if something was trying to push me over to the edge. I finally snapped out of it, put a few of my own thoughts inside my head and got the hell out of there. I haven't gone back to the Elsinore since. I sensed whatever's there is very evil. I kept hearing, "Come back, come back " as I walked down the balcony steps. I found Jeff downstairs after I worked my way through the crowd. Before I left the theater, its true nature came out, and the entity became way more aggressive.

"Get back up here and jump, you stupid ass bitch."

That was the last message I heard as I walked out the door.

Luckily, Jeff understood the need to miss the comedy show.

"What the hell came over you back there?"

"I'm so sorry, that wasn't me. I had no reason to be angry at you. I think something evil took over. Jeff, I felt like I was being possessed."

"Julie, do you really expect me to believe that?"

"It tried to convince me to jump off the balcony."

Jeff apologized for doubting me, picked up my hand and held it all the way to the car. It was very comforting. Jeff finally believed me. We really didn't talk much more about it, and he's never asked me to go back. I think we both just needed time to process it all.

Sometimes there just aren't any words.

A few days later I researched the Elsinore Theater. I was shocked by what I learned. The upper balcony is haunted by a female spirit, who fell from the ledge to her death. It's also rumored the be haunted by a boy who was killed in the men's bathroom. Some people claim they saw blood reflected in the mirror. Where is this bathroom located? On the balcony, of course. Whatever was going on in this place, I'll never go back. It makes me a little sad because they have a lot of great concerts I miss out on, but it's just not worth the risk. I believe the murder of the little boy attracted a demon, maybe even the same demon who tried to end my life.

People are the same in death as they were in life. There are both good and evil spirits. I have had some scary moments with unsavory spirits in my home. I allow the good spirits to remain and tell the dangerous ones they have to leave, they're not welcome. Most of the time it works. When it doesn't, I annoy them by burning sage. Demons and evil spirits hate the smell of burned sage. Sage is an exceptional tool.

Protect yourself. Some spirits have a lot of power and can cause harm to the living. So, if a person is bad in life, chances are they will still be bad in the afterlife. I've also learned how to do some mental rituals to turn off communication. I set an intention that I don't want to be bothered by anyone, living or dead. I picture it like turning off a light switch. It works better with the dead than it does with the living.

Something caught my eye one day while watching television. I usually sit on the same couch when I watch TV. It was a sunny day so I could see my own reflection on the television screen. I could also see the reflection of our backyard on the screen. I didn't see anything until I looked away, but when I looked back at the screen, I saw a man standing in our backyard who wasn't there a moment ago. I blinked hard and looked again. He was standing in front of a fir tree, but the strangest part was, our fence is at least eight feet tall and he towered above it. Plus, his head was double the size of the tree trunk.

I paused the television so I could see what was happening without having to look directly at him. I stared in disbelief until eventually he just faded away. He never moved or changed expression. He reminded me of, "Lurch" from the Addams Family, a sitcom from the 60's. The only thing I knew for sure, he wasn't of this world. Aside from that, he's still a mystery.

I can also see spirit animals. I saw the Shih Tzu we rescued from an abusive neighbor a few months after she died. I was on the floor blocking a blanket I had just finished crocheting. Baby used to lick her paws a lot when she was alive. I could hear her licking before I actually saw her. I said, "Baby, stop licking" and she did.

I can see both people and animal spirits. It used to be, the only way I knew they were spirits is because they were completely transparent. However, I only see animals as transparent spirits these days. Now I'm able to see dead people as full-bodied apparitions that look as solid as any other living person. I also see them in color. Only once did I see a decomposing spirit. Luckily, that only happened one time.

I've also been able to see spirits on television. *It's fascinating.* I was watching the televised funeral of George H. W. Bush from the National Cathedral in Washington, D.C. I was watching dignitaries, past presidents *and first ladies* walk up the steps and enter the Cathedral. Then I noticed something off to the right. I was looking at George and Barbara standing side by side watching the same people.

No kidding, I couldn't believe it myself.

They appeared to be making comments and occasionally laughing at some of the people as they passed by. I was really taken by how much fun they appeared to be having. Barbara had a smile on her face the entire time. She wore a blue dress and George was wearing a black suit. Barbara was also wearing her signature white pearl necklace. It warmed my heart seeing the two of them having such a great time together.

Just another day in the life of an accidental medium.

42

There are so many questions still left unanswered.

Questions like . . . why was my family's name written in the Bible? Also, why do I have the weirdest ancestors? They are all on the Brannan side of the family, too. To recap, William Brannan was a serial killer in Washington State, another was the first millionaire in California. His name was Sam Brannan. He's very famous still in the Sacramento area. There's even a bar named after him called "Brannan Manor." One of these days I hope to visit the area. Who knows, maybe good old Sam will inspire me to write a book about him. From what I've been told, he was a very colorful character. He was friends with Brigham Young, who later had to kick Sam out of the church for, "A general course of unchristian-like conduct, neglect of duty, and for combining with lawless assemblies to commit murder and other crimes."

Looks like it might run in the family.

Then there's the crazy great, *not sure how many greats* grandma who became ultra-rich from some oil wells her family owned in Texas. Not sure how that happened. She considered money to be the "Root of all evil." She lived in a cabin by the river and supposedly buried a large sum of her money. This brings me to yet another family mystery.

Supposedly, nutty grandma invested fifty million in a bank some-where. If it's true, this money has been earning interest for over 150 years. Could there still be a ton of money in a bank somewhere? Another family legend claims that some had gotten close to cracking the mystery. When they got a little too close to the money, they were paid off handsomely to walk away. *Just weird.* I don't think I will ever solve this mystery.

I've struggled financially most of my life. I'd love to be the one to crack the case, but hoping to someday find this money is just wishing upon a star. It's fun to wish sometimes, but I don't know where I'd even begin. My mother gave me some papers her father kept in a file. He was trying very hard to find the money and even hired a few lawyers. There's lots of speculation and correspondence between family members in the file, but nothing concrete.

Is it just a family legend?

It wasn't an accident I was brought to this location and had the experiences I did. It's all part of a grand plan. We may never know until we cross over, but I've been told our entire life is mapped out before we're even born. Not only our lives, but other people who play a part in our life journey have to agree to the plan as well. It's all very detailed and connected.

Being touched by the paranormal can change lives. I believe it has to do with acceptance. It challenges everything you once thought was real. I've really come a long way in my paranormal journey. Today I feel fortunate to have my gift. I know things most people have to die first to learn. I've been through a lot of scary stuff, but I've come to realize how truly amazing my gift is. I've learned to honor my abilities, not fear them.

There's a lot out there in the Universe we still don't understand. What's the big secret and meaning of life? I've been told by my spirit guides, we are here mainly to learn. I believe this experience has helped me enjoy life more and to understand that death isn't some-thing to fear. There IS life after death. I've heard many spirits refer to it as, "going home."

My life view used to be very black and white. The many incredible experiences I've had have completely rocked my belief system. Being a skeptic is no longer an option for me. I know spirits are everywhere, and they know that I can see them.

Even though I've grown stronger and I don't fear as much anymore, I'm still careful with what I mess with. I don't touch Ouija boards, ever. I feel it's very dangerous to play with a Ouija board. It's risky because you just don't know what doors you're opening or who you're communicating with. Most of the time, low-level entities come through or worse. It can unleash evil entities, or even demons. I don't "poke the bear" so to speak, or mess around with things I don't understand. Another thing I never do is provoke spirits. I don't recommend provoking, especially evil entities. These things are powerful beyond our own comprehension, so approach them with the utmost of caution.

Just because I have more access than most into the spirit realm, doesn't mean I'm an evil person. I have a very strong faith in God. Some people have harshly judged me for being able to see and communicate with the spirit world. I think people fear what they don't understand. I'm guilty of that myself. I've had angels help me many times and I often pray. Whenever something frightens me, all I need to do is pray. I went from being fearful all the time . . . to fearless. I'm not a victim anymore, I'm a survivor.

Why is it so active here? I believe it's because of all the energy surrounding the property. Deaths at the rock crushing quarry, the forgotten cemetery and the angry Indian spirits because of the desecration of their most sacred burial ground, their effigy mounds.

Many souls passed through here. Some went to the other side, but others couldn't. This location became a hotbed for activity. It can intensify emotions, feelings, even creative abilities. Because I'm so sensitive and "in-tune" with spirit, I was able to pick up on the energies right away.

It was my awakening.

Even though I was vulnerable at first, it became a positive turning point in my life. I was often afraid, but at the same time, I found healing in this house. My spirit guides also guided me to write my books here.

Now, instead of being terrified, I feel guided by the spirit world and my life has never been better. My self-esteem has improved, I've put an end to my self-destructive ways and righted my wrongs. I broke the cycle of abuse and raised an amazing daughter here.

There's a big mystical Universe out there. We are never alone. There are unseen forces that are always here, helping us navigate through our lives.

That's the good news. Spirits on the other side push us to take positive steps. Sometimes the spirit world shakes us straight and puts us on the right path toward our destiny. Spirits really do work in mysterious ways. There's so much more to this world than we know. Keep your mind open and it just might surprise you.

Today I feel more empowered than ever before. I feel like I'm a soldier preparing for my next battle. Or, perhaps I'll be called upon to help lead a lost spirit into the light.

I don't know what, when or where, but now, I'm finally ready.

As for me, I will continue to be . . .

Haunted.

Dear Reader,

Thank you for taking the time to read *Haunted: A Paranormal Awakening*. I sincerely hope you enjoyed reading about my paranormal journey.

What's next? Stay tuned, because the paranormal saga continues with a historical twist in my next book, *Sam*.

As an author, I love feedback... so tell me what you liked, what you loved, even what you didn't like. I'd love to hear from you.

You can write me at connect@juliecoons.com and visit me on the web at www.juliecoons.com. You can also find me on Facebook.

Don't forget to sign up for my newsletter so you can be the first to get advanced notifications of book releases.

Thank you so much for reading *Haunted* and for spending time with me.

In gratitude,
Julie Coons

~

LEAVE A REVIEW

Finally, if you're so inclined, I'd love it if you would post a review of *Haunted*. Reviews can be tough to come by these days, and you, the reader, have the power to make or break a book. You can go online and leave a review on my Amazon or Goodreads page, which also feature my other titles.

ABOUT THE AUTHOR

Award-winning author Julie Coons lives in a small town in Oregon. *This Does Not Leave This House* was her debut memoir. Amy's bookshelf reviews awarded it the #1 position for Top 10 Books of 2018. Her second book, *Why She Lied*, is based on a true story and winner of the 2019 Readers' Favorite International Book Award bronze medal. Her third book, *Haunted: A Paranormal Awakening*, is also a true story about Julie's paranormal journey. Julie plans to stay in the paranormal genre for a while.

Made in the USA
Las Vegas, NV
23 November 2021

35170331R00164